Math Mammoth
Grade 3
Skills Review Workbook

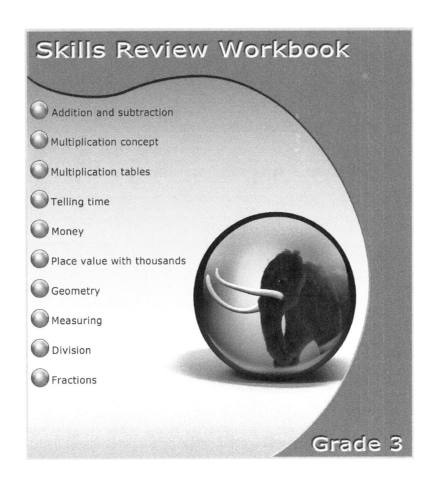

By Maria Miller

Contents

Chapter 4: Telling Time

Chapter 5: Money

Chapter 6: Place Value with Thousands

Chapter 7: Geometry

Chapter 8: Measuring

Chapter 9: Division

Chapter 10: Fractions

Foreword

Math Mammoth Grade 3 Skills Review Workbook has been created to complement the lessons in *Math Mammoth Grade 3* complete curriculum. It gives the students practice in reviewing what they have already studied, so the concepts and skills will become more established in their memory.

These review worksheets are designed to provide a spiral review of the concepts in the curriculum. This means that after a concept or skill has been studied in the main curriculum, it is then reviewed repeatedly over time in several different worksheets of this book.

Some exercises are marked as optional. This means they are beyond the Common Core Standards for 3rd grade.

This book is divided into chapters, according to the corresponding chapters in the *Math Mammoth Grade 3* curriculum. You can choose exactly when to use the worksheets within the chapter, and how many of them to use. Not all students need all of these worksheets to help them keep their math skills fresh, so please vary the amount of worksheets you assign your student(s) according to their needs.

Each worksheet is designed to be one page, and includes a variety of exercises in a fun way without becoming too long and tedious.

The answer key is provided as a separate file.

I wish you success in teaching math!

Maria Miller, the author

Skills Review 1

1. Find the skip-counting pattern and complete the chart. Then color according to the directions.

5			14			23			
					50				
	68								

   a. Color yellow all of the even numbers in the fifth column from the right.

   b. Color green all of the odd numbers in the ninth column from the left.

   c. Color pink all of the even numbers in the second column from the left.

   d. Color purple all of the odd numbers in the eighth column from the right.

2. First add or subtract mentally, and then color.

13 - 9 = blue
27 + 5 = yellow
32 - 4 = pink
14 + 9 = gray
50 - 6 = orange
48 + 7 = red
16 - 8 = green
25 + 6 = brown

3. Write an addition or a subtraction for each problem. Use ? for the unknown thing.

a. Damian put 25 baby chicks in a box. Seven of them jumped out and ran back to the chicken coop. How many are still in the box?	**b.** Clarice bought a hat for $7 and a blouse for $15, and now she has $23 left. How much money did she have originally?
_____	_____
Solution: _____	Solution: _____

Skills Review 2

1. Write the Roman numerals using normal numbers.

a.	b.	c.	d.
XVIII	CXIV	XLII	CCLXX

2. Complete the puzzle.

22	−		=	16
+				
	−		=	61
=		+		−
92				
		=		=
	+	24	=	54

3. Subtract mentally.

a. $281 - 9$
b. $173 - 4$
c. $520 - 6$
d. $352 - 7$

4. Match the correct additions and/or subtractions with the problem.

Jacob has 100 cows. Some of them are brown and 53 are black and white. How many are brown?	$100 + \underline{?} = 53$	$53 + \underline{?} = 100$
	$100 - 53 = \underline{?}$	$100 + 53 = \underline{?}$

5. Write an addition or a subtraction <u>using ? for the unknown</u> to match the problem.

A factory has 154 employees. Sixty of them are men. How many employees are women?

Skills Review 3

1. Add an ending (th, st, nd, rd) so you get an ordinal number. Write or say the ordinal number.

a. 24___   _____

b. 3___   _____

c. 42___   _____

d. 71___   _____

2. Add 50 each time (repeatedly).

_430_

_480_

_____

_____

_____

_____

_____

3. Subtract and continue the pattern.

210 – 2 = _____

215 – 4 = _____

220 – 6 = _____

_____ – ___ = _____

_____ – ___ = _____

_____ – ___ = _____

4. Write the numbers in the grids and add.

a. 42 + 219 + 126

b. 8 + 537 + 13

c. 205 + 34 + 112

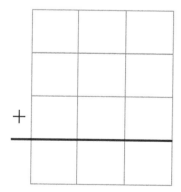

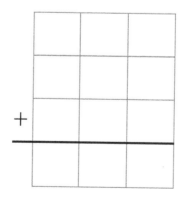

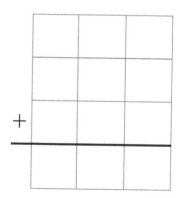

5. Add or subtract.

a.	b.	c.
744 + 50 = _____	577 – 30 = _____	968 + 20 = _____

Skills Review 4

1. Add.

a.
```
  5 9 3
+   5 6
```

b.
```
  2 7 8
+   2 3
```

c.
```
  6 5 9
+ 2 6 4
```

d.
```
  3 9 7
+ 3 1 7
```

2. A challenge!

  -40 -8 -6 -30 -9 -10

250 _____ _____ _____ _____ _____ _____

3. Write using Roman numerals.

a. 153	**b.** 79	**c.** 56
d. 345	**e.** 18	**f.** 124

4. Write $<$, $>$ or $=$.

a. $370 + 25$ ☐ $400 - 5$ b. $630 + 54$ ☐ $790 - 7$

c. $948 - 30$ ☐ $910 + 20$ d. $68 + 4$ ☐ $80 - 9$

5. Solve the problems.

Jasmine sold 23 tickets for a school play, Nathan sold 12, and Brad sold 8.

a. How many more tickets did Jasmine sell than Brad?

b. How many tickets did the three children sell in total?

Skills Review 5

1. Subtract. You will need to regroup. Find the answers in the number queue below.

a.	b.	c.	d.
$\begin{array}{r} 6\ 7\ 1 \\ -\ 1\ 3\ 5 \\ \hline \end{array}$	$\begin{array}{r} 7\ 5\ 8 \\ -\ 4\ 6\ 2 \\ \hline \end{array}$	$\begin{array}{r} 5\ 4\ 9 \\ -\ 2\ 7\ 8 \\ \hline \end{array}$	$\begin{array}{r} 9\ 2\ 6 \\ -\ 5\ 8\ 6 \\ \hline \end{array}$

The number queue: 8 5 3 7 5 3 6 9 2 0 8 1 3 4 0 7 4 2 9 6 0 3 8 5 4 0 2 7 1 0 4 9 1

2. Solve what number goes in place of the triangle.

a. $\triangle - 12 = 29$

$\triangle =$ _____

b. $760 - \triangle = 743$

$\triangle =$ _____

c. $349 - \triangle = 310$

$\triangle =$ _____

3. Add 5 to each number on the bottom. Notice the pattern!

10	12	14	16	18	20	22	24	26	28	30

4. Match the correct additions and/or subtractions with the problem.

Gwen bought a laptop for $435 and Jeff bought one for $9 less. How much did Jeff pay for his laptop?

$9 + \underline{\ ?\ } = 435$

$\underline{\ ?\ } - 9 = 435$

$435 + 9 = \underline{\ ?\ }$

$435 - 9 = \underline{\ ?\ }$

5. Solve the word problem.

Bianca, Craig, and Ethan played a board game.
Bianca got 95 points and Ethan got 60.

Craig had 137, but then he lost 60 points when he landed on a penalty square.
How many points did the children get in total?

Skills Review 6

1. On Friday, Al's Ice Cream Shop sold 18 strawberry cones, 22 chocolate cones, and 28 vanilla cones. Make a pictograph to show this! Draw one ice cream cone picture to mean **4 ice cream cones**. Draw a picture of a half ice cream cone to mean **2 ice cream cones**.

	Ice Cream Cones Sold	
chocolate		
vanilla		
strawberry		

2. **a n b s y r a t o e w p**

Circle the fourth letter from the right.

Circle the twelfth letter from the left.

Circle the eighth letter from the right.

Circle the second letter from the left.

What word can you make with these letters?

_____

3. Add.

a. $146 + 7 =$ _____

b. $398 + 9 =$ _____

c. $754 + 6 =$ _____

4. Regroup twice. Then subtract.

a. Take 1 ten and regroup that with the ones.	Next, take 1 hundred and regroup that with the tens.	Now you can subtract.

$$700 + 30 + 4$$
$$- \quad 400 - 80 - 9$$

→

$$700 + 20 + \rule{1cm}{0.3cm}$$
$$- \quad 400 - 80 - 9$$

→

$$600 + \rule{1cm}{0.3cm} + \rule{1cm}{0.3cm}$$
$$- \quad 400 - 80 - 9$$

b. Take 1 ten and regroup that with the ones.	Next, take 1 hundred and regroup that with the tens.	Now you can subtract.

$$500 + 20 + 2$$
$$- \quad 200 - 30 - 9$$

→

$$500 + 10 + \rule{1cm}{0.3cm}$$
$$- \quad 200 - 30 - 9$$

→

$$400 + \rule{1cm}{0.3cm} + \rule{1cm}{0.3cm}$$
$$- \quad 200 - 30 - 9$$

Skills Review 7

1. Match.

XIV	93
XXXVIII	253
CCLIII	14
CXXIV	38
XCIII	47
XLVII	124

2. Write an addition or a subtraction for each problem. Use ? for the unknown thing.

a. There were 24 cows in a pasture. Then, 16 cows escaped through a hole in the fence. How many cows were left in the pasture? _____ Solution: _____	**b.** Melissa baked 35 cookies. Then, Jenna baked some more cookies and now, there are 59 cookies in total. How many cookies did Jenna bake? _____ Solution: _____

3. Skip-count by fives.

432	437			

Puzzle Corner Find single-digit numbers in place of the shapes so that the additions are true. Note that the same symbol means the same number in both places.

$$
\begin{array}{r}
4 \ \bigcirc \ \square \\
+ \ 4 \ \ 3 \ \bigcirc \\
\hline
9 \ \ 2 \ \ 4
\end{array}
$$

$$
\begin{array}{r}
5 \ \square \ \triangle \\
+ \ \triangle \ \ 3 \ \ 8 \\
\hline
9 \ \ 0 \ \ 1
\end{array}
$$

Skills Review 8

1. Subtract. Check by adding.

a.	b.
$\begin{array}{r} 6\ 3\ 4 \\ -\ 3\ 9\ 7 \end{array}$ $+$ _____	$\begin{array}{r} 8\ 1\ 2 \\ -\ 2\ 3\ 8 \end{array}$ $+$ _____

2. Add or subtract.

a. $352 + 50 =$ _____	b. $548 + 40 =$ _____	c. $779 - 30 =$ _____

3. Solve what number goes in place of the triangle.

a. $\triangle + 42 = 60$ $\triangle =$ _____	b. $345 - \triangle = 339$ $\triangle =$ _____	c. $83 + \triangle = 92$ $\triangle =$ _____

4. Solve the word problems.

a. Richard drove 125 miles to Grandma's
house and Jeremy drove 109 miles.
How many miles in total did they drive
round-trip?

b. Paul caught 15 fish and Randy caught 17.
They shared them equally. How many fish
did each boy get?

The boys met Mrs. Hill on their way home and
they gave her half of the total number of fish.
How many fish does each boy have now?

Skills Review 9

1. Number the men with ordinal numbers starting *from the right*. Use the picture to help answer the questions.

   a. Mr. Johnson is 5th in the line. Mr. Williams is behind him and there are six people between them. What is Mr. Williams' position in the line?

   b. Mr. Davis is 9th in the line. Mr. Anderson is ahead of him and there are four people between them. What is Mr. Anderson's position in the line?

2. Regroup twice. First, regroup a hundred as 10 tens. Then, regroup a ten as 10 ones. Then subtract.

a. Take 100 and regroup that as 10 tens.	Next, take 1 ten and regroup that as 10 ones.	Now you can subtract.
$800 + 0 + 5$ $-\ 300 - 30 - 9$ $\rightarrow$	$700 + \boxed{} + 5$ $-\ 300 - 30\ - 9$ $\rightarrow$	$700 + \boxed{} + \boxed{}$ $-\ 300 - 30\ - 9$
b. $500 + 0 + 2$ $-\ 200 - 40 - 8$ $\rightarrow$	$400 + \boxed{} + 2$ $-\ 200 - 40 - 8$ $\rightarrow$	$400 + \boxed{} + \boxed{}$ $-\ 200 - 40 - 8$

3. Add mentally, in parts.

a. $39 + 53$	**b.** $68 + 25$	**c.** $74 + 36$
$= 30 + 50 + 9 + 3$ $=$ _____	$=$ _____	$=$ _____

Skills Review 10

1. Add or subtract.

a.
```
  2 1 9
  3 5 6
+   7 8
```

b.
```
  4 4 5
−   6 9
```

c.
```
  1 3 6
  4 8 3
+ 3 7 7
```

d.
```
  7 9 4
− 4 4 8
```

2. Add up to find the differences.

a.	b.	c.	d.
72 − 39 = _____	51 − 17 = _____	63 − 25 = _____	86 − 41 = _____

3. Compare. Write <, >, or = in the box.

a. XIV + VI ☐ XVIIII

b. LXXIV − XL ☐ XC − LVI

c. XC − XL ☐ XXX + XL

d. XLIX + XXI ☐ CIV − XL

4. Solve the word problems.

a. Farmer John has 102 goats. One day, they escaped from their pasture. After chasing them for 45 minutes, Farmer John had caught 68 of them. How many goats did he have left to catch?

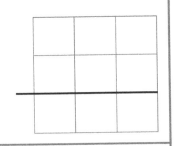

b. Janice had lots of stickers in her collection. Then, her grandma gave her 40 more for her birthday, but 6 of them got lost. Now Janice has 272 stickers.

How many stickers did she have initially?

Skills Review 11

1. Subtract. Check by adding.

a.	b.
7 0 0 − 3 2 8　　+ _____	9 0 5 − 4 6 7　　+ _____

2. Add the same number each time (repeatedly).

Add 30.
_450_
_480_
_____
_____
_____
_____

3. Write an addition or a subtraction for each problem. Use ? for the unknown thing.

a. Ashley has $49. She wants to buy a skateboard that costs $62. How much more money does Ashley need?

_____

Solution: _____

b. Danny harvested 33 carrots and put them in a basket. Some hungry rabbits came along and gobbled up 14 of the carrots. How many carrots are left?

_____

Solution: _____

4. Find *about* how much the two things cost together. Use rounded numbers!

a. a kite, $28, and camera, $42	b. shoes, $59, and a game, $33	c. a fan, $64, and a book, $25
kite about $_____	shoes about $_____	fan about $_____
camera about $_____	game about $_____	book about $_____
together about $_____	together about $_____	together about $_____

Skills Review 12

1. Add an ending (th, st, nd, rd) so you get an ordinal number. Write the ordinal number.

a. 13____ _____   **b.** 22____ _____

c. 51____ _____   **d.** 90____ _____

2. Write the numbers in the grid and add.

$$48 + 413 + 5 + 151$$

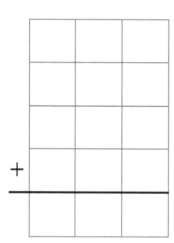

3. Subtract and continue the pattern.

220 – 5 = _____

220 – 10 = _____

220 – 15 = _____

_____ – ____ = _____

_____ – ____ = _____

_____ – ____ = _____

4. Round these numbers to the nearest whole ten.

a. $33 \approx$ _____   **b.** $67 \approx$ _____   **c.** $95 \approx$ _____   **d.** $44 \approx$ _____

Puzzle Corner   What numbers are missing from the subtraction problems?

```
  □ 2 □          9 □ □          8 □ 8          □ 3 5
- 2 □ 7        - □ 3 5        - □ 7 □        - 3 □ □
───────        ───────        ───────        ───────
  4 5 4          6 4 8          3 9 2          5 6 3
```

Skills Review 13

1. Subtract.

a.	b.	c.	d.
7 0 2 − 2 5 4	8 0 0 − 4 3 1	4 0 7 − 1 6 9	6 0 0 − 3 8 4

2. Write using Roman numerals.

a. 24	**b.** 49	**c.** 99	**d.** 67
25	50	100	68
26	51	101	69

3. Solve the problems. Write a "how many more" addition and a subtraction to match them.

a. Carmen swam for 45 minutes and Erica swam for 29 minutes. How much longer did Carmen swim than Erica?

_____ + _____ = _____

_____ − _____ = _____

b. Mr. Jenkins is 72 and Alex is 15. How much older is Mr. Jenkins than Alex?

_____ + _____ = _____

_____ − _____ = _____

4. Write the previous and the next whole ten, then round the number.

a. _____, 254, _____ 254 ≈ _____	b. _____, 867, _____ 867 ≈ _____	c. _____, 306, _____ 306 ≈ _____

5. Find the skip-counting pattern and complete the chart.

231		221							

Skills Review 14

1. How many miles is it from Ferry Bluff to Peck's Landing?

	Ferry Bluff	Mazomanie	Arena	Hwy 14	Peck's Landing	Otter Creek	Lone Rock	Gotham
Sauk City	5	6	11	21	23	31	32	36
Ferry Bluff		1	6	11	18	24	25	31
Mazomanie			7	16	17	23	24	30
Arena				10	12	18	19	25

2. *About* how many miles is it from Sauk City to Gotham? Round your answer to the nearest ten miles.

3. Find the difference between:

a. 17 and 62	**b.** 341 and 892	**c.** 520 and 960

4. Estimate the total cost.

a. a table, $374, and chair, $129	**b.** a skate board, $57, sun glasses, $32
table about $_____	a skate board about $_____
chair about $_____	sun glasses about $_____
total cost about $ _____	total cost about $ _____

5. Solve the word problems.

a. Farmer Jacobs had 342 sheep. Then, he sold 89 of them at an auction. How many sheep does he have left?	**b.** Mr. Bell had 32 students, Mrs. Cox had 29, and Miss Allen had 40. Then, seven of Mr. Bell's students transferred to a different school. How many students do the three teachers have in total now?

Skills Review 15

1. Compare the chart with the pictograph. Each flower picture means 6 flowers. Half of a flower picture means 3 flowers. Is the pictograph correct? If not, cross out the incorrect pictures and draw the correct ones.

Flowers Picked	
Rhoda	15
Stephanie	27
Karen	9

Flowers Picked	
Rhoda	🌸🌸🌸
Stephanie	🌸🌸🌸🌸🌸
Karen	🌸🌸🌸

2. A train stopped at Witty City and 9 people got off. Then it stopped at Clown Town and 20 people got on. Now there are 223 passengers on the train. How many passengers were on the train before it stopped at Witty City?

3. Calculate.

a. $(17 - 9) - (4 + 3) =$ _____	**b.** $(700 - 60) - (80 - 30) =$ _____
$17 - 9 - 4 + 3 =$ _____	$700 - 60 - 80 - 30 =$ _____

4.

   a. How many seahorses are there between the 4th seahorse and the 11th?

   b. How many seahorses are there between the 2nd seahorse and the 8th?

5. A subtraction challenge!

a. $104 -$ _____ $= 95$	**b.** _____ $- 30 = 15$	**c.** _____ $- 147 = 50$

Skills Review 16

1. The bar graph shows how many seashells some children found at the beach.

   a. Who found the most seashells?

   _____

   b. How many more seashells did Sandra find than Alicia?

   _____

   c. How many seashells did Jacob and Kelvin find in total?

   _____

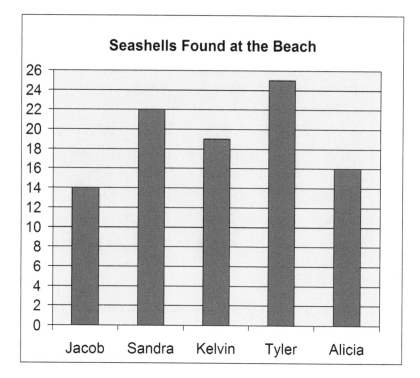

Seashells Found at the Beach

2. Add.

a.		b.		c.		d.	
	7 9		3 9 0		3 2 5		4 2
	3 0 4		4 5 6		1 8 3		2 7 5
	2 6 7		1 3 3		1 4 7		8
+	2 5	+	1 1	+	2 0 5	+	4 6 3

3. Add and subtract using Roman numerals. Write your answer as a Roman numeral.

   a. XV + VI   **b.** CXXIII − L   **c.** CCXX + LX

   d. XXXII − XIV   **e.** LIV + XVI   **f.** CL − IX

4. Subtract in parts.

a. $382 - 7$	**b.** $574 - 9$	**c.** $763 - 6$
$382 - \underline{\ 2\ } - \underline{\ \ \ }$	$574 - \underline{\ \ \ } - \underline{\ \ \ }$	$763 - \underline{\ \ \ } - \underline{\ \ \ }$
$= \underline{\ \ \ }$	$= \underline{\ \ \ }$	$= \underline{\ \ \ }$

Skills Review 17

1. Estimate the total cost.

a. a painting, $435, and flute, $574 painting about $_____ flute about $_____ total cost about $ _____	**b.** a calendar, $15, and curtains, $74 a calendar about $_____ curtains about $_____ total cost about $ _____

2. Write one addition and two subtraction sentences to match the model.

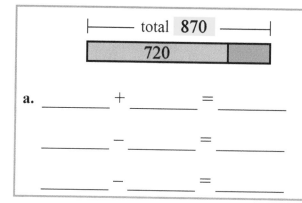

a. _____ + _____ = _____

_____ − _____ = _____

_____ − _____ = _____

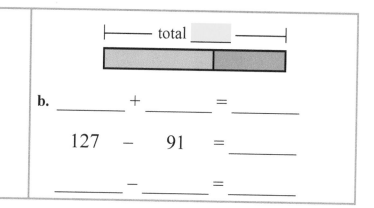

b. _____ + _____ = _____

127 − 91 = _____

_____ − _____ = _____

3. Write an addition or a subtraction for each problem. Use ? for the unknown thing.

a. Alex collected 17 eggs from the henhouse. Then Mom used 9 eggs to make 3 cakes. How many eggs are left? _____ Solution: _____	**b.** Cheryl had $78. Then her mom gave her some money and she now has $90. How much money did her mom give her? _____ Solution: _____

4. Draw to illustrate the multiplication. Remember, the symbol ✖ is read "times."

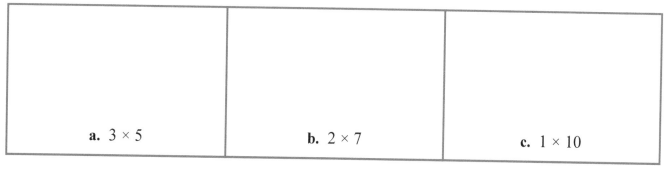

a. 3×5	**b.** 2×7	**c.** 1×10

Skills Review 18

1. Add parentheses to each equation to make it true.

| **a.** $12 - 4 + 6 = 2$ | **b.** $17 - 3 - 5 - 2 = 11$ | **c.** $23 - 9 + 6 - 2 = 18$ |

2. You make a round trip from Arena to Lone Rock. How many miles is that?

3. How much farther is the distance between Arena and Gotham than the distance between Mazomanie and Hwy 14?

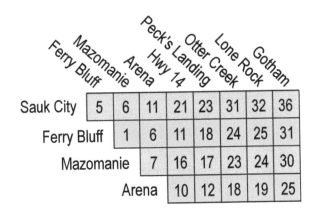

	Ferry Bluff	Mazomanie	Arena	Hwy 14	Peck's Landing	Otter Creek	Lone Rock	Gotham
Sauk City	5	6	11	21	23	31	32	36
Ferry Bluff		1	6	11	18	24	25	31
Mazomanie			7	16	17	23	24	30
Arena				10	12	18	19	25

4. Subtract. Check by adding.

```
    7 0 5
  – 6 7 8    + _____
  _____
```

5. Add the same number each time.

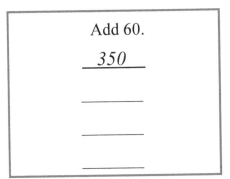

Add 60.

_350_

_____

_____

_____

6. Write an addition and a multiplication sentence for each picture.

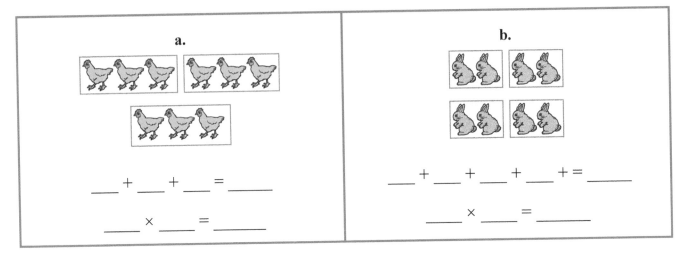

a.

___ + ___ + ___ = _____

_____ × _____ = _____

b.

___ + ___ + ___ + ___ + ___ = _____

_____ × _____ = _____

Skills Review 19

1. Add an ending (th, st, nd, rd) so you get an ordinal number. Write the ordinal number.

   a. 11____ _____ **b.** 43____ _____

   c. 61____ _____ **d.** 72____ _____

2. Draw jumps to fit the multiplication problem.

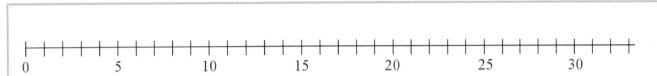

   a. $4 \times 6 =$ _____

   b. $3 \times 3 =$ _____

3. Max caught 22 crickets, Tim caught 18, and Aaron caught 7 fewer than Max. How many crickets did the boys catch in total?

4. **a.** Fill in.

   Sweet Treat Bakery used _____ lb of apples.

   b. Draw apples in the pictograph for the different bakeries.

   Toothy's Bakery used 20 lb.
   Choo Choo Bakery used 16 lb.
   Hungry Hat Bakery used 28 lb.

Apples Used to Make Pies	
Toothy's Bakery	
Choo Choo Bakery	
Hungry Hat Bakery	
Sweet Treat Bakery	🍎🍎🍎🍎🍎🍎🍎

🍎 = 4 pounds of apples

Skills Review 20

1. Add or subtract.

a.
```
    6 4 5
  + 2 9 7
```

b.
```
    8 0 2
  - 5 6 9
```

c.
```
    3 3 8
  + 3 2 3
```

d.
```
    9 1 7
  - 4 5 8
```

2. Write an addition and a multiplication to match the picture.

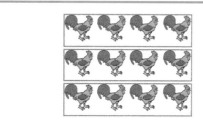

a. _____

_____

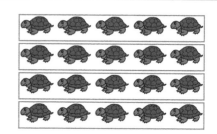

b. _____

_____

3. Write the Roman numerals using normal numbers.

a. LIV   b. CLXX   c. CXIV   d. XCVIII

e. XCIII   f. XLIX   g. XLVII   h. CCLX

4. Solve what number goes in place of the triangle.

a. $\triangle - 70 = 43$

$\triangle = $ _____

b. $525 - \triangle = 455$

$\triangle = $ _____

c. $\triangle - 90 = 635$

$\triangle = $ _____

5. Find the skip-counting pattern and continue it.

397			388	

Skills Review 21

1. Calculate. Circle the operation to be done first.

a. $12 + 4 \times 5$	**b.** $2 \times 7 - 3 \times 3$	**c.** $10 - 5 + 2 \times 4$

2. Chloe has 158 marbles and Brenna has 233. About how many marbles do they have altogether? Use rounded numbers.

3. Round the numbers to the nearest whole ten.

a. $429 \approx$ _____	**b.** $325 \approx$ _____	**c.** $113 \approx$ _____	**d.** $644 \approx$ _____

4. Solve.

a. How many fingers do five people have?
b. Three cows and one chicken have a total of how many legs?
c. How many tires do three cars and two bicycles have?

5. Match the correct addition and subtraction with the problem.

Maria baked some cookies. She gave 48 to the Johnson family and now she has 60 left. How many cookies did Maria bake?	$60 + 48 = \underline{?}$ $60 - \underline{?} = 48$	$\underline{?} + 48 = 60$ $\underline{?} - 48 = 60$

6. Add mentally, in parts.

a. $\qquad 48 + 53$	**b.** $\qquad 26 + 37$
$=$ $=$	$=$ $=$

Skills Review 22

1. The Gill Family went on a short road trip to visit some parks. Draw the bars for the bar graph.

Day	Miles Traveled
Monday	115
Tuesday	80
Wednesday	105
Thursday	70

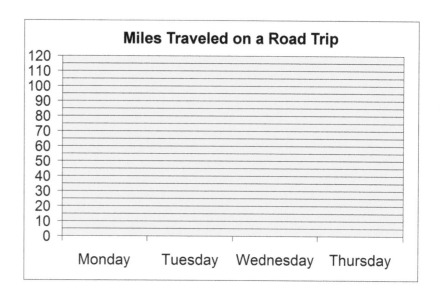

2. Add repeatedly (or skip-count) to multiply. You can use the number line to help.

| **a.** $4 \times 5 =$ _____ | **b.** $3 \times 6 =$ _____ | **c.** $5 \times 2 =$ _____ | **d.** $2 \times 7 =$ _____ |

3. Solve the problems. Write a number sentence for each problem.

a. Kelly, Megan, and Christy each have five rabbits and Faye has seven. How many rabbits do the four girls have in total?

b. Andrew and his two brothers each bought six pens and they put them all in a box on the shelf. Their pet cat, Tuna, knocked the box off of the shelf and now nine pens are missing. How many pens are left in the box?

c. Jamison had $72. Then, he bought two flashlights for $7 each and a watch for $27. How much money does he have now?

Skills Review 23

1. <u>About</u> how many miles is a round trip from Veggie Village to Pickle Point?

2. Layla drove from Toy Truck Town to Chocolateville, from there to Mt. Muffin, and then back to Toy Truck Town. How many miles did she drive in total?

	Toy Truck Town	Veggie Village	Chocolateville	Binky's Bluff	Hamster Hill	Mt. Muffin	Cricket Corner	Pickle Point
Silly City	7	12	19	26	32	48	55	71
Toy Truck Town		4	9	13	21	24	37	42
Veggie Village			8	11	17	22	30	49
Chocolateville				12	19	27	41	56

3. Round the numbers to the nearest ten.

a. $623 \approx$ _____	**b.** $88 \approx$ _____	**c.** $212 \approx$ _____	**d.** $41 \approx$ _____
$496 \approx$ _____	$52 \approx$ _____	$734 \approx$ _____	$75 \approx$ _____

4. Make a word problem to match the picture.

Puzzle Corner   Find single-digit numbers in place of the shapes so that the addition and the subtraction are true. Note that the same symbol means the same number in both places.

```
    5  ◯ ▭
 +  1  7  ◯
 ─────────
    7  4  5
```

```
    6  ▭ △
 -  △  4  4
 ─────────
    2  9  9
```

Skills Review 24

1. Draw X's and group them in two ways to illustrate the two ways to multiply.

a.

_____ × _____ = _____
seven groups of 4

_____ × _____ = _____
four groups of 7

b.

_____ × _____ = _____
three groups of 8

_____ × _____ = _____
eight groups of 3

2. Calculate. Circle the operation to be done first. Parentheses → multiply → add/subtract.

a. $16 - 4 \times 3$	**b.** $5 \times (3 - 2) + 3$	**c.** $12 + 2 \times (3 + 3)$

3. Solve the problems.

a. Eight pairs of doves landed in a tree. Then three of the pairs flew away. How many doves are still in the tree?

b. Tanya made a decoration for her sister's room with five rows of five seashells, and now she has 58 left. How many seashells did she have originally?

c. Mr. Anderson had 102 beautiful fruit trees. Then one day, there was a bad thunderstorm and afterwards only 63 trees were still standing. How many trees were knocked down by the storm?

Skills Review 25

1. Color: 73 = yellow
   24 = purple
   37 = orange
   64 = blue
   76 = pink

2. Calculate. Circle the operation to be done first.

a. $8 + 4 \times 3 + 21$	**b.** $2 \times (2 + 7)$	**c.** $3 \times (11 - 3) - 2$

3. Add or subtract.

a.
$$\begin{array}{r} 5\ 4\ 7 \\ -\ 3\ 2\ 9 \\ \hline \end{array}$$

b.
$$\begin{array}{r} 3\ 6\ 9 \\ +\ 1\ 2\ 4 \\ \hline \end{array}$$

c.
$$\begin{array}{r} 8\ 0\ 2 \\ -\ 5\ 7\ 6 \\ \hline \end{array}$$

d.
$$\begin{array}{r} 2\ 4\ 8 \\ +\ 3\ 7\ 6 \\ \hline \end{array}$$

4. Write a number sentence for the problems and solve.

   a. Each of four pet chickens ate five ounces of corn, and a fifth chicken ate only three ounces. How many ounces of corn did they eat in total?

   b. At that same rate, how many ounces of corn would the chickens eat in a week?

5. Solve the word problem.

Farmer Jones has 362 chickens. Some are brown, some are black, and some are white. If 120 are brown and 82 are white, how many are black?

Skills Review 26

1. The pictograph shows how many elephants are in four different herds. Each represents 6 elephants.

Elephants in Various Herds	
Herd 1	🐘 🐘 🐘
Herd 2	🐘 🐘 🐘 🐘 🐘
Herd 3	🐘 🐘
Herd 4	🐘 🐘 🐘 🐘 🐘 🐘

   a. Fill in.

   Herd 4 has _____ elephants.

   b. How many more elephants does Herd 2 have than Herd 3? _____

   c. Herd 1 and Herd 4 have _____ elephants altogether.

2. Write each multiplication as an addition.

   a. $5 \times 6 =$ _____

   b. $8 \times 3 =$ _____

3. Vanessa bought a red dress for $72 and a blue dress for $58. What was the difference in price of the two dresses?

4.

   Number the people above with ordinal numbers starting *from the left*.

   a. How many people are between the ninth person and the fourth person? _____

   b. How many people are between the sixth person and the second person? _____

5. Multiply.

a. $0 \times 0 =$ _____	**b.** $1 \times 8 =$ _____	**c.** $0 \times 4 =$ _____	**d.** $9 \times 1 =$ _____

Skills Review 27

1. Don't write the answers down. Use these problems for random drill practice.

$\square \times 2 = 14$ $\square \times 2 = 12$ $\square \times 2 = 6$ $\square \times 2 = 8$ $\square \times 2 = 10$

$\square \times 2 = 18$ $\square \times 2 = 16$ $\square \times 2 = 22$ $\square \times 2 = 20$ $\square \times 2 = 24$

2. Multiply.

a. $2 \times 2 = $ _____	b. $2 \times 5 = $ _____	c. $9 \times 2 = $ _____	d. $2 \times 11 = $ _____

3. Write an addition sentence then write a multiplication sentence multiplying by 2 to double it.

a. Double 9	b. Double 14	c. Double 16
____ + ____ = _____	____ + ____ = _____	____ + ____ = _____
____ × ____ = _____	____ × ____ = _____	____ × ____ = _____

4. Add and subtract using Roman numerals. Write your answer as a Roman numeral.

    a. XLIV + LVI   b. CLX − XXXIIII   c. LXII − XV

5. Subtract in parts.

a. $373 - 7$	b. $115 - 8$	c. $612 - 5$
$373 - $ ____ $- $ ____	_____ $- $ ____ $- $ ____	_____ $- $ ____ $- $ ____
$= $ _____	$= $ _____	$= $ _____

6. Write the multiplication sentence that is illustrated by the jumps on the number line.

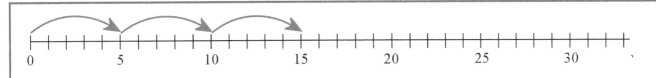

____ × _____ = _____

Skills Review 28

1. Add or subtract.

a.	b.	c.	d.	e.
7 0 3 − 3 7 5	4 1 0 − 1 9 6	2 3 6 + 4 4 8	9 0 1 − 3 8 4	5 4 2 + 2 6 9

2. Add the same number each time.

a. Add 25.	b. Add 30.
_130_	_185_
_155_	_215_
_____	_____
_____	_____
_____	_____

3. Write a word problem about bicycle tires and car tires to match this addition and multiplication:

$3 \times 4 + 9 \times 2 =$ _____

4. **a.** Multiply by 4.

a.

$3 \times 4 =$ ____	$4 \times 4 =$ ____
$8 \times 4 =$ ____	$11 \times 4 =$ ____
$6 \times 4 =$ ____	$1 \times 4 =$ ____
$12 \times 4 =$ ____	$10 \times 4 =$ ____
$9 \times 4 =$ ____	$5 \times 4 =$ ____
$2 \times 4 =$ ____	$7 \times 4 =$ ____

b. Fill in the missing factors.

b.

____ $\times 2 = 12$	____ $\times 2 = 6$
____ $\times 2 = 20$	____ $\times 2 = 2$
____ $\times 2 = 8$	____ $\times 2 = 22$
____ $\times 2 = 24$	____ $\times 2 = 16$
____ $\times 2 = 4$	____ $\times 2 = 10$
____ $\times 2 = 14$	____ $\times 2 = 18$

5. Solve. Write a number sentence, not just the answer!

Seven girls and two boys bought two pairs of shoes each.
How many individual shoes did they buy in total?

Skills Review 29

1. Review the table of ten. Check yourself with these problems.

a.	b.	c.	d.
$10 \times 9 =$ _____	$10 \times 8 =$ _____	$6 \times 10 =$ _____	$3 \times 10 =$ _____
$7 \times 10 =$ _____	$4 \times 10 =$ _____	$10 \times 2 =$ _____	$10 \times 0 =$ _____
$5 \times 10 =$ _____	$10 \times 10 =$ _____	$11 \times 10 =$ _____	$12 \times 10 =$ _____

2. Write a number sentence for the total cost.

$5 $5 $5 $35

_____

3. Solve. Write a calculation (multiplication, addition, or subtraction) for each problem.

a. Kim has $7 and Dan has ten times as much money.
How much money do they have together?

b. Dan lost $12. How much money does he
have now?

4. Subtract whole tens and whole hundreds mentally.

a.	b.	c.
$78 - 30 =$ _____	$439 - 70 =$ _____	_____ $- 50 = 248$
$78 - 50 =$ _____	$439 - 40 =$ _____	_____ $- 90 = 248$

Puzzle Corner Which operations will make the number sentences true?

$6 \ \square \ 3 \ \square \ 2 = 0$ $9 \ \square \ 3 \ \square \ 3 = 24$ $8 \ \square \ 4 \ \square \ 7 \ \square \ 6 = 30$

Skills Review 30

1. Don't write the answers down. Use these problems for random drill practice.

$\square \times 5 = 35$ $\square \times 5 = 20$ $\square \times 5 = 55$ $\square \times 5 = 40$ $\square \times 5 = 30$

$\square \times 5 = 5$ $\square \times 5 = 45$ $\square \times 5 = 25$ $\square \times 5 = 50$ $\square \times 5 = 15$

2. Round the numbers to the nearest ten.

a. $45 \approx$ _____

b. $613 \approx$ _____

c. $52 \approx$ _____

d. $757 \approx$ _____

3. Continue the pattern.

$5 \times 1 - 2 =$ _____

$5 \times 2 - 4 =$ _____

___ $\times$ ___ $-$ ___ $=$ _____

___ $\times$ ___ $-$ ___ $=$ _____

___ $\times$ ___ $-$ ___ $=$ _____

4. Solve. Write a number sentence for each problem.

a. Mom bought four packages of markers that had three markers in each package and five packages of markers that had six markers in each package. How many markers did Mom buy?

b. Caleb worked for three hours helping his neighbor clean up her yard. The neighbor paid him $10 an hour. After Caleb got paid, he went to the store and bought a puzzle for $15. How much money does he have left?

Puzzle Corner

Lisa placed sticks in piles of five on the ground. Her dogs ran off with all of the sticks from two of the piles and now she has 35 sticks left. How many piles of sticks did she have originally?

Skills Review 31

1. <u>About</u> how many miles is it round-trip from Ho Hum Hill to Pasta Peak?

	Ho Hum Hill	Anteater Alley	Lizard Landing	Vinegarville	Cheddarfield	Pasta Peak	Oopsburg	Raisin Ridge
Giggletown	124	129	136	152	167	175	179	203
Ho Hum Hill		113	121	140	155	169	182	194
Anteater Alley			137	154	178	183	195	217
Lizard Landing				152	174	181	200	226

2. Adam drove from Anteater Alley to Oopsburg. Cindy drove from Giggletown to Cheddarfield. Who drove more miles?

   How many more?

3. **a.** Multiply by 3.   **b.** Fill in the missing factors.

a.

7 × 3 = _____	12 × 3 = _____
11 × 3 = _____	9 × 3 = _____
2 × 3 = _____	5 × 3 = _____
6 × 3 = _____	3 × 3 = _____
10 × 3 = _____	8 × 3 = _____
4 × 3 = _____	1 × 3 = _____

b.

_____ × 4 = 4	_____ × 4 = 24
_____ × 4 = 28	_____ × 4 = 8
_____ × 4 = 44	_____ × 4 = 32
_____ × 4 = 12	_____ × 4 = 48
_____ × 4 = 36	_____ × 4 = 16
_____ × 4 = 20	_____ × 4 = 40

4. Solve. Write a number sentence for the problem. You can also draw pictures to help!

Dawn baked some cookies and packaged them in boxes with ten in each box. She filled eight boxes and had four cookies left over. How many cookies did she bake?

Skills Review 32

1. The bar graph shows how many miles some people drive to work.

   a. Calculate how many miles Mia drives to work and back. Then do the same for Forrest.

   _____ and _____

   b. How many miles does Bruce drive to work and back in three days?

   _____

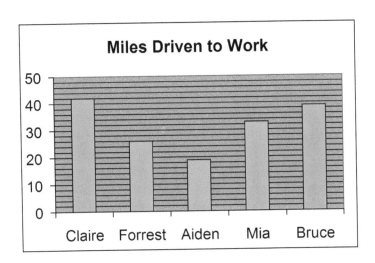

Miles Driven to Work

2. Below the addition, write a matching subtraction problem so that the numbers in the boxes are the same. Can you use mental math? Try adding up!

   a. 283 + ☐ = 315

   _____ − _____ = ☐

   b. 45 + ☐ = 92

   _____ − _____ = ☐

3. Review the table of six. Then check yourself with these problems.

a.	b.	c.	d.
2 × 6 = _____	5 × 6 = _____	1 × 6 = _____	12 × 6 = _____
7 × 6 = _____	4 × 6 = _____	6 × 6 = _____	8 × 6 = _____
10 × 6 = _____	9 × 6 = _____	11 × 6 = _____	3 × 6 = _____

4. Find the missing factors.

a.	b.	c.	d.
_____ × 3 = 12	_____ × 3 = 9	_____ × 3 = 3	_____ × 3 = 36
_____ × 3 = 18	_____ × 3 = 33	_____ × 3 = 15	_____ × 3 = 30
_____ × 3 = 24	_____ × 3 = 6	_____ × 3 = 27	_____ × 3 = 21

Skills Review 33

1. Solve. Write a number sentence for each problem.

a. Max bought two packages of walnuts and shared some of them with his friends. Afterwards, there was only about half of one package of walnuts left, or 25 walnuts. About how many walnuts were in the two packages originally?

b. Make up a *multiplication* word problem that has to do with people and slices of pizza. Then solve it.

c. Mom picked lots of lemons in the orchard, and used 14 of them to make lemonade. Little Joe counted the lemons that were left; there were 229. How many lemons did Mom pick?

2. Complete the table.

_____ × 11 = 132

_____ × 11 = 66

_____ × 11 = 121

_____ × 11 = 88

_____ × 11 = 33

_____ × 11 = 77

3. Compare the expressions and write < or >.

a. 4×11 ☐ 7×6

b. 5×7 ☐ 3×11

c. 12×5 ☐ 8×11

d. 2×11 ☐ 3×7

e. 11×5 ☐ 9×6

f. 9×11 ☐ 10×10

g. 7×10 ☐ 6×11

h. 9×9 ☐ 7×11

I'm in the table of 3! If you take 5 away from me, you will get a number that is in the table of 11.

Mystery Number

Skills Review 34

1. Multiply.

a. $1 \times 5 =$ _____	**b.** $0 \times 3 =$ _____	**c.** $1 \times 10 =$ _____	**d.** $7 \times 1 =$ _____
$0 \times 0 =$ _____	$1 \times 9 =$ _____	$0 \times 10 =$ _____	$8 \times 0 =$ _____

2. Use ? for the unknown amount.

a. Greg filled several glasses with juice. After 23 people each drank a glass of juice, there were 9 left. How many glasses did Greg fill? _____ Solution: _____	**b.** Rachel practiced the violin for 47 minutes and Jim practiced the flute for 53 minutes. How much longer did Jim practice than Rachel? _____ Solution: _____

3. Skip-count by nines. Also practice it backwards (up-down).

0, 9, _____, _____, _____, _____, _____, _____, _____, _____, _____, _____, 108

4. Multiply.

a.	**b.**	**c.**	**d.**
$2 \times 9 =$ _____	$5 \times 9 =$ _____	$12 \times 9 =$ _____	$6 \times 9 =$ _____
$7 \times 9 =$ _____	$3 \times 9 =$ _____	$8 \times 9 =$ _____	$9 \times 9 =$ _____
$11 \times 9 =$ _____	$10 \times 9 =$ _____	$4 \times 9 =$ _____	$1 \times 9 =$ _____

5. Solve the problem. Write a calculation (multiplication and/or addition and/or subtraction). You can also draw pictures to help!

Beth divided her 36 stuffed animals between 9 of her friends. How many stuffed animals did each one get? _____ × _____ = _____

Skills Review 35

1. Multiply.

a.	b.	c.	d.
$7 \times 9 = $ _____	$7 \times 12 = $ _____	$7 \times 7 = $ _____	$7 \times 2 = $ _____
$7 \times 4 = $ _____	$7 \times 8 = $ _____	$7 \times 5 = $ _____	$7 \times 11 = $ _____
$7 \times 1 = $ _____	$7 \times 3 = $ _____	$7 \times 10 = $ _____	$7 \times 6 = $ _____

2. Add or subtract.

a.
```
  3 5 9
+   7 2
```

b.
```
  8 0 1
−   3 5
```

c.
```
  6 0 8
+ 1 9 6
```

d.
```
  9 3 4
− 2 4 7
```

3. Write a *multiplication* for each problem.

a. Allen and two of his friends equally shared 12 crackers.
How many crackers did each one get?

_____ × _____ = _____

b. How many wheels do six tricycles have?

_____ × _____ = _____

4. Write the two multiplication sentences that are indicated by the arrows.

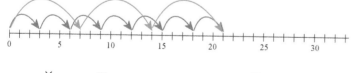

_____ × _____ = _____   _____ × _____ = _____

5. Write using Roman numerals.

a. 23	b. 15	c. 58	d. 104
24	16	59	107

Skills Review 36

1. Multiply by 8. Then find the missing factors.

a.

$5 \times 8 =$ ____	$8 \times 8 =$ ____
$12 \times 8 =$ ____	$11 \times 8 =$ ____
$3 \times 8 =$ ____	$7 \times 8 =$ ____
$1 \times 8 =$ ____	$4 \times 8 =$ ____
$9 \times 8 =$ ____	$10 \times 8 =$ ____
$6 \times 8 =$ ____	$2 \times 8 =$ ____

b.

____ $\times 7 = 28$	____ $\times 7 = 7$
____ $\times 7 = 70$	____ $\times 7 = 63$
____ $\times 7 = 49$	____ $\times 7 = 84$
____ $\times 7 = 21$	____ $\times 7 = 14$
____ $\times 7 = 56$	____ $\times 7 = 77$
____ $\times 7 = 35$	____ $\times 7 = 42$

2. Calculate. Be careful!

a. $18 - 9 + 5 \times 3$	b. $8 \times (6 + 2) - 28$

3. Add an ending (th, st, nd, rd) so you get an ordinal number. Write or say the ordinal number.

a. 73____ _____

b. 5____ _____

c. 51____ _____

d. 22____ _____

4. Solve what number goes in place of the triangle.

a. $72 - \triangle = 49$	b. $\triangle - 150 = 245$	c. $591 - \triangle = 490$
$\triangle =$ _____	$\triangle =$ _____	$\triangle =$ _____

5. Solve the problem. Write a number sentence.

Mrs. Mills has to print off eight worksheets for each of her nine students that she tutors and six extra worksheets. What is the total number of worksheets she need to print?

Skills Review 37

1. Multiply.

a.	b.	c.	d.
$4 \times 12 =$ _____	$5 \times 12 =$ _____	$6 \times 12 =$ _____	$8 \times 12 =$ _____
$7 \times 12 =$ _____	$11 \times 12 =$ _____	$9 \times 12 =$ _____	$12 \times 12 =$ _____
$10 \times 12 =$ _____	$2 \times 12 =$ _____	$1 \times 12 =$ _____	$3 \times 12 =$ _____

2. Subtract. Be careful with regrouping! Find the answers in the number queue below.

a.
$$\begin{array}{r} 9\ 0\ 5 \\ -\ 7\ 4\ 8 \\ \hline \end{array}$$

b.
$$\begin{array}{r} 6\ 4\ 2 \\ -\ 1\ 9\ 5 \\ \hline \end{array}$$

c.
$$\begin{array}{r} 4\ 2\ 1 \\ -\ 3\ 2\ 6 \\ \hline \end{array}$$

d.
$$\begin{array}{r} 7\ 0\ 4 \\ -\ 2\ 8\ 9 \\ \hline \end{array}$$

1 9 3 0 9 5 2 0 0 1 9 3 4 4 7 2 0 1 5 2 9 4 1 5 3 0 9 2 1 5 1 5 7 0 3 5 2 9 8

3. Convert between feet and inches.

a. 1 foot = 12 inches	**b.** 60 inches = _____ ft	**c.** 108 inches = _____ ft
5 feet = _____ inches	8 ft = _____ in.	12 ft = _____ inches

4. Skip-count backwards.

144, 132, _____, _____, _____, _____, _____,

_____, _____, _____, _____, _____, _____

5. Match the correct addition and subtraction with the problem.

a. Adam is 27 years old and Barry is 34 years older than him. How old is Barry?	$34 - \underline{?} = 27$	$\underline{?} - 34 = 27$
	$27 + \underline{?} = 34$	$27 + 34 = \underline{?}$
b. Two weeks ago, Sonya had $61. Now, she has $23 less. How much money does she have now?	$23 + \underline{?} = 61$	$\underline{?} + 23 = 61$
	$61 - 23 = \underline{?}$	$\underline{?} - 23 = 61$

Skills Review 38

1. Write the numbers in the grids and add.

   a. $382 + 5 + 237$ **b.** $42 + 118 + 7 + 371$ **c.** $129 + 26 + 253 + 4$

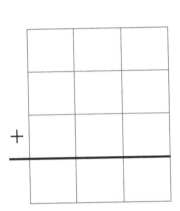
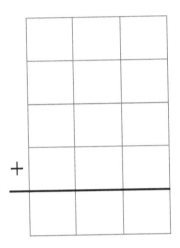
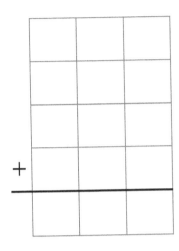

2. Write the time the clock shows. Then write the time 5 minutes *earlier* in the box beneath.

	_____ : _____
5 min. earlier →	_____ : _____

3. Write a *multiplication* word problem that has to do with bags of fruit.

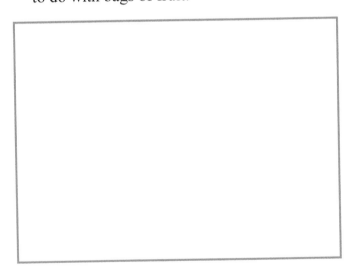

4. Estimate the total cost.

a. a mirror, $45, and vase, $22 mirror about $_____ vase about $_____ total cost about $_____	**b.** fishing rod, $123, and tent, $467 fishing rod about $_____ tent about $_____ total cost about $_____

Skills Review 39

1. A challenge!

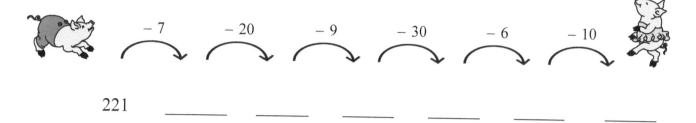

221 _____ _____ _____ _____ _____ _____

2. Practice multiplying by 2 and by 10.

a.	b.	c.	d.
$9 \times 2 =$ _____	$3 \times 10 =$ _____	$7 \times 2 =$ _____	$5 \times 10 =$ _____
$7 \times 10 =$ _____	$6 \times 2 =$ _____	$12 \times 10 =$ _____	$4 \times 2 =$ _____
$11 \times 2 =$ _____	$9 \times 10 =$ _____	$3 \times 2 =$ _____	$11 \times 10 =$ _____

3. Write the time using "a quarter past," "a quarter till," "half past," or "o'clock."

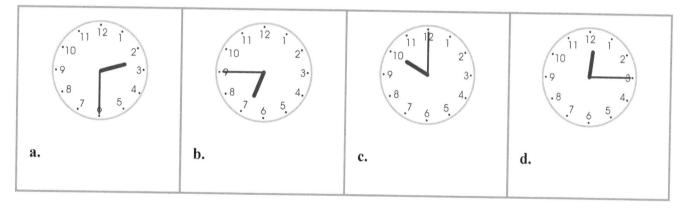

a.   b.   c.   d.

4. Write a number sentence that is illustrated by the jumps on the number line.

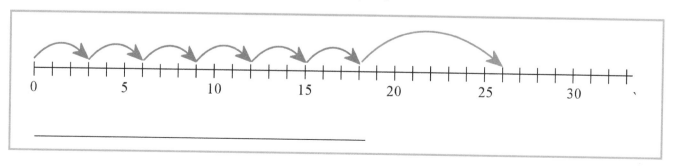

_____

Skills Review 40

1. The pictograph shows the amount of different kinds of fruit that are for sale at a fruit stand. Each fruit picture equals 6 kg. Each half of a fruit picture equals 3 kg.

   a. How many more kilograms of bananas are there than strawberries?

   _____

   b. How many kilograms of oranges and apples does the stand have in total?

   _____

Fruit for Sale	
Apple	
Banana	
Orange	
Strawberry	
Pear	

2. Multiply.

a. $10 \times 12 =$ _____	**b.** $1 \times 717 =$ _____	**c.** $0 \times 309 =$ _____	**d.** $111 \times 2 =$ _____

3. Write the time the clock shows using the words "quarter past," "quarter till," "past," or "till."

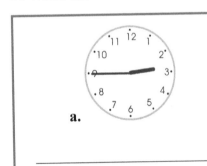

a. _____

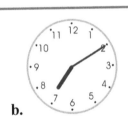

b. _____

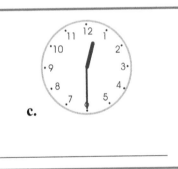

c. _____

4. Write one addition and two subtraction sentences to match the model.

a.

total 573
375

_____ + _____ = _____

_____ − _____ = _____

_____ − _____ = _____

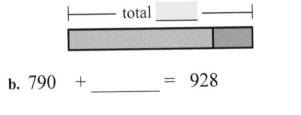

b. 790 + _____ = 928

_____ − _____ = _____

_____ − _____ = _____

Skills Review 41

1. Underline or circle whether the number is even or odd. If the number is even, write it as "two times the number that was doubled." If the number is odd, do nothing.

a. **19** is even/odd	b. **24** is even/odd	c. **16** is even/odd
2 × _____	2 × _____	2 × _____

2. Find the missing factors.

a.	b.	c.	d.
_____ × 5 = 35	4 × _____ = 20	5 × _____ = 45	_____ × 4 = 16
_____ × 5 = 50	4 × _____ = 48	_____ × 5 = 10	_____ × 4 = 44
_____ × 5 = 15	4 × _____ = 12	5 × _____ = 60	_____ × 4 = 36

3. The clock shows the time now. Write the later times.

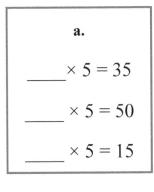

NOW:

- 5 minutes later _____ : _____
- 10 minutes later _____ : _____
- 20 minutes later _____ : _____
- 25 minutes later _____ : _____

4. Daniel has 122 marbles, some blue and some green. If 63 are blue, how many are green?

5. Find the skip-counting pattern and continue it.

183		195		

6. Add and subtract using mental math.

a. 261 − 7 = _____	b. 68 + 9 = _____	c. 532 − 5 = _____

Skills Review 42

1. Write the two multiplication sentences that are indicated by the arrows.

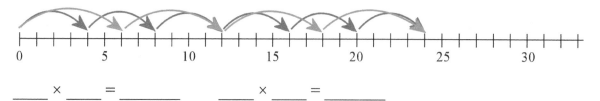

____ × ____ = _____   ____ × ____ = _____

2. Calculate. Circle the operation to be done first.

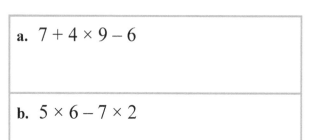

a. $7 + 4 \times 9 - 6$

b. $5 \times 6 - 7 \times 2$

3. Write the time the clock shows.

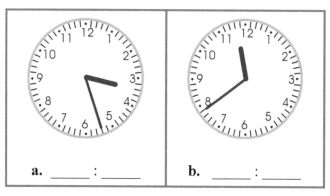

a. ____ : ____   **b.** ____ : ____

4. Solve. Write a number sentence for each problem.

a. Lilly baked three cakes and used three eggs in each one. Jasmine baked five cakes and used two eggs in each one. How many eggs did the two women use in total?

b. Willow invited some people to a party. Twelve people were sick, so only nine were able to come, but each of the nine brought her a gift so she was happy. How many people did Willow invite to her party?

c. Vince bought seven bags of apples that had eight apples in each bag. One of the bags broke and seven apples fell out. How many apples are still in bags?

Skills Review 43

1. Compare. Write <, >, or = in the box.

   a. LXXIV + LV ☐ 129   **b.** LXVII − XXXX ☐ CXX − LXVI

   c. XCIV − XXXV ☐ XX + XL   **d.**   61 ☐ CIV − XXXX

2. How many minutes is it?

a. From 7:12 till 7:35	**b.** From 1:23 till 1:48	**c.** From 12:07 till 12:51

3. The bar graph shows how many points some children got while playing a game.

   a. Which two players *combined points* were 76 points more than Roger's?

      _____ and _____

   b. Make another question about the bar graph. Write it here and solve it.

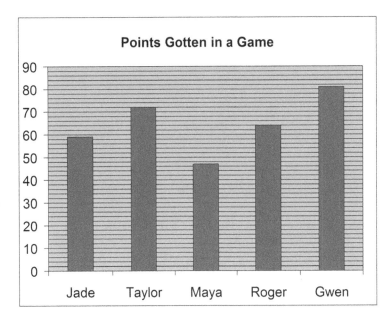

Points Gotten in a Game

4. Review the tables of three and eleven. Then check yourself with these problems.

a.	**b.**	**c.**	**d.**
9 × 11 = ____	2 × 3 = ____	11 × 11 = ____	4 × 3 = ____
7 × 11 = ____	6 × 3 = ____	12 × 11 = ____	12 × 3 = ____
10 × 11 = ____	10 × 3 = ____	4 × 11 = ____	5 × 3 = ____

Skills Review 44

1.

    a. Henrietta is third in the line. Rocket is behind her and there are three animals between them. What is Rocket's position in the line?

    b. Mustard is ninth in the line. Hamster is ahead of him and there are six animals between them. What is Hamster's position in the line?

2. Calculate.

a. $(16 - 4) \times (3 + 6) =$ _____	**b.** $(230 - 50) - (70 - 40) =$ _____
$16 - 4 \times 3 + 6 =$ _____	$230 - 50 - 70 - 40 =$ _____

3. Kelly practiced on the violin for 45 minutes and finished at 3:35. What time did she start?

4. Add or subtract.

    a. $\begin{array}{r} 8\ 0\ 3 \\ -\ 3\ 4\ 7 \\ \hline \end{array}$ **b.** $\begin{array}{r} 4\ 3\ 6 \\ +\ 2\ 6\ 5 \\ \hline \end{array}$ **c.** $\begin{array}{r} 7\ 2\ 1 \\ -\ 5\ 5\ 9 \\ \hline \end{array}$ **d.** $\begin{array}{r} 3\ 4\ 6 \\ +\ 4\ 9\ 8 \\ \hline \end{array}$

5. Draw jumps on the number line to illustrate the problem.

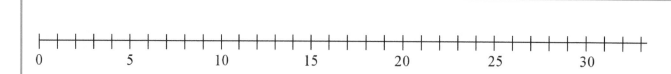

$5 + 7 \times 3 =$ _____

Skills Review 45

1. Write the time the clock shows. Then write the time 10 minutes later in the box beneath.

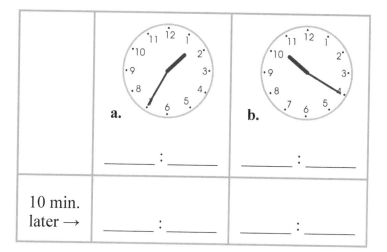

	a.	b.
	_____ : _____	_____ : _____
10 min. later →	_____ : _____	_____ : _____

2. Add the same number each time.

a. Add 40.	b. Add 15.
_219_	_65_
_259_	_80_
_____	_____
_____	_____
_____	_____
_____	_____

3. Round the numbers to the nearest whole ten.

a. 532 ≈ _____	b. 985 ≈ _____	c. 57 ≈ _____	d. 613 ≈ _____

4. Melissa was supposed to go skiing in the mountains on December 29th, but she decided to go two weeks early. When did she go skiing?

5. Brad went to visit his grandma on June 23rd and returned home on July 12th. How long did he visit his grandma?

6. Alex has three bags with seven oranges in each one. Conrad has five bags with four oranges in each one.

   Who has more oranges?   How many more?

7. Find the missing factors.

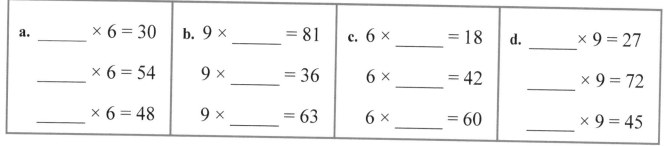

a. _____ × 6 = 30	b. 9 × _____ = 81	c. 6 × _____ = 18	d. _____ × 9 = 27
_____ × 6 = 54	9 × _____ = 36	6 × _____ = 42	_____ × 9 = 72
_____ × 6 = 48	9 × _____ = 63	6 × _____ = 60	_____ × 9 = 45

Skills Review 46

1. Solve what number goes in place of the triangle.

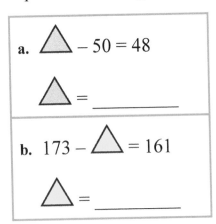

a. $\triangle - 50 = 48$

$\triangle =$ _____

b. $173 - \triangle = 161$

$\triangle =$ _____

2. How much money? Write the amount in cents.

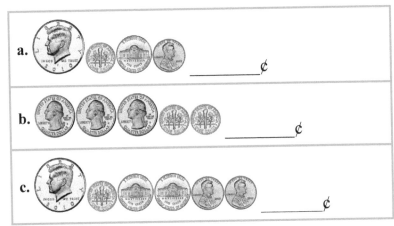

a. _____ ¢

b. _____ ¢

c. _____ ¢

3. Jason started working at 7:30 a.m. and finished at 6:00 p.m. How many hours did he work?

4. Eight of Veggie Village's inhabitants moved to Chocolateville. Then, five people moved from Pickle Point to Veggie Village, and now Veggie Village has 233 inhabitants. How many inhabitants did it have originally?

5. Write a number sentence for the problem, and solve.

How many more legs do three goats have than seven snakes?

_____

 **Puzzle Corner**   Which operations will make the number sentences true?
Hint: You may need to add parentheses.

5 ☐ 9 ☐ 8 = 37   72 ☐ 4 ☐ 12 = 24   9 ☐ 4 ☐ 4 ☐ 7 = 64

17 ☐ 6 ☐ 8 = 65   43 ☐ 8 ☐ 6 = 29   13 ☐ 6 ☐ 3 ☐ 5 = 26

Skills Review 47

1. Write the times using hours:minutes.

a. a quarter till 11	**b.** half past 7	**c.** a quarter past 3	**d.** a quarter till 9
_____ : _____	_____ : _____	_____ : _____	_____ : _____

2. Review the tables of twelve and seven. Then check yourself with these problems.

a.	**b.**	**c.**	**d.**
$2 \times 12 =$ _____	$4 \times 7 =$ _____	$7 \times 12 =$ _____	$8 \times 7 =$ _____
$6 \times 12 =$ _____	$11 \times 7 =$ _____	$12 \times 12 =$ _____	$12 \times 7 =$ _____
$9 \times 12 =$ _____	$5 \times 7 =$ _____	$4 \times 12 =$ _____	$3 \times 7 =$ _____

3. Solve the problem. Write a "how many more" addition and a subtraction to match it.

Caleb's mother wants him to practice the flute for an hour. He has already practiced for 23 minutes. How many more minutes does he need to practice?

_____ + _____ = _____

_____ − _____ = _____

4. Find the difference between:

a. 18 and 43	**b.** 762 and 800	**c.** 155 and 380

5. How much money? Write the amount.

a. $ _____

b. $ _____

Skills Review 48

1. Find the change.

a. A pizza costs $11.50. You give $20.	b. A doll costs $8.45. You give $10.	c. Sunglasses cost $22.25. You give $30.
Change: $_____	Change: $_____	Change: $_____

2. The pictogram that shows how many birds Carl saw on certain days.
   Each 🐦 represents 7 birds.

   a. How many more birds did Carl see on Tuesday than on Thursday?

   b. On which two days did Carl see a total of 42 birds *combining the two days*?

Birds Carl Saw	
Monday	🐦🐦🐦
Tuesday	🐦🐦🐦🐦🐦🐦
Wednesday	🐦🐦🐦🐦
Thursday	🐦🐦

3. Solve. Write a number sentence for each problem. Don't just write the answer.

   a. Farmer Jacobson has four pastures with nine cows in each pasture. Farmer Smith has six pastures with seven cows in each pasture. Which farmer has more cows?

   How many more?

   b. Megan baked 84 rolls and put them in bags, with 12 in each bag. How many bags of rolls did she have?

   Oops! Baby brother sat on two of the bags of rolls and squashed them flatter than a pancake! How many good rolls does Megan have left?

   c. Mr. Miller shared his watermelon harvest with six of his neighbors. He gave four to each one, and afterwards he had 17 left over. How many watermelons did he harvest?

Skills Review 49

1. Write the time in words. Use the expressions "quarter past," "quarter till," "till," or "past."

   a. 9:30 _____   **b.** 11:15 _____

   c. 7:35 _____   **d.** 2:45 _____

2. Review the table of eight. Then check yourself with these problems.

a.	**b.**	**c.**	**d.**
$2 \times 8 =$ _____	$5 \times 8 =$ _____	$1 \times 8 =$ _____	$4 \times 8 =$ _____
$7 \times 8 =$ _____	$3 \times 8 =$ _____	$6 \times 8 =$ _____	$9 \times 8 =$ _____
$10 \times 8 =$ _____	$12 \times 8 =$ _____	$8 \times 8 =$ _____	$11 \times 8 =$ _____

3. Write any multiplication problem you like where the answer is between 10 and 32. Write it in two ways. Then draw jumps on the number line to illustrate.

_____ $\times$ _____ = _____   _____ $\times$ _____ = _____

4. Find the total cost of buying the items listed. Add mentally if you can.

 $2.25	$6.50	$3.15	$4.90	$1.40

a. kite and ball	**b.** car and teddy bear	**c.** ball, crayons, and car

Skills Review 50

1. Add. In (b), write the numbers carefully under each other and then solve.

a.

$$
\begin{array}{r}
\$3.80 \\
8.32 \\
6.29 \\
+\ 4.76 \\
\hline
\end{array}
$$

b. $51.78 + $0.83 + $17.95 + $2.41

2. Multiply.

| **a.** $0 \times 432 =$ _____ | **b.** $5 \times 6 =$ _____ | **c.** $1 \times 264 =$ _____ | **d.** $2 \times 12 =$ _____ |

3. Color.

XXVIIII = light blue
CCLXXVII = purple
XLI = brown
CCXCVII = pink
LXXXVIII = yellow
CCLXVIIII = dark green
XXXII = red
CCCLXXXI = light green
CXLVI = gray
LXXVIII = dark blue
LIIII = orange
CXXIII = yellow

4. Compare the expressions and write $<$, $>$, or $=$.

a. 2×7 ☐ 3×5 **b.** 4×6 ☐ 3×8 **c.** 8×5 ☐ 7×5

d. 5×8 ☐ 7×6 **e.** 10×7 ☐ 7×11 **f.** 6×12 ☐ 12×9

5. How many minutes pass? Subtract (or figure out the difference).

from	5:15	12:07	7:41	2:24	10:38
to	5:43	12:22	7:55	2:39	10:56
minutes					

Skills Review 51

1. The chart shows the population for each city. Draw bars on the graph to show each population *approximately*.

Populations	
Poplar City	673
Oaktown	438
Pine Village	289
Elmsville	517
Cedar Point	365

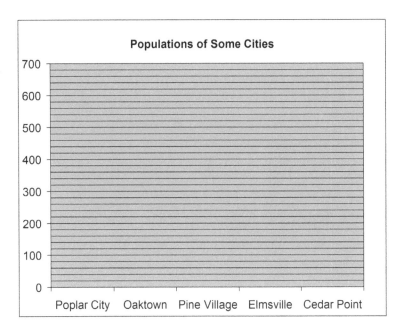

Populations of Some Cities

2. Fill in the table.

a. Six thousand two hundred five	thou-sands	hund-reds	tens	ones		b. Two thousand sixty-three	thou-sands	hund-reds	tens	ones

3. Shirley bought a purse for $17.50 and a brush for $5.75. What was Shirley's change from $30?

4. Write the time the clock shows, and the time given 25 minutes later.

	a. _____ : _____	b. _____ : _____	c. _____ : _____	d. _____ : _____
25 min. later				

Skills Review 52

1. Multiply.

a.	b.	c.	d.
$6 \times 8 =$ _____	$9 \times 5 =$ _____	$2 \times 6 =$ _____	$3 \times 11 =$ _____
$3 \times 2 =$ _____	$4 \times 12 =$ _____	$10 \times 8 =$ _____	$7 \times 4 =$ _____
$8 \times 12 =$ _____	$11 \times 7 =$ _____	$1 \times 9 =$ _____	$5 \times 10 =$ _____

2. It takes Carolyn 45 minutes to clean her room.
   If she wants to finish at 3:20, what time does
   she need to start?

3. Add an ending (th, st, nd, rd) so you get an ordinal number. Write or say the ordinal number.

   a. 12_____ _____

   b. 42_____ _____

   c. 81_____ _____

   d. 93_____ _____

4. Make a word problem to match the addition sentence $343 + \triangle = 400$, and solve it.

5. These numbers are written as sums, but in a scrambled order! Write them as normal numbers.

a. 4 thousand 8 ones 7 tens	**b.** 5 tens 1 hundred 9 thousand

I am in the table of three but not in the table of six.
My tens digit is double my ones digit. Who am I?

Skills Review 53

1. Amelia drove from Ho Hum Hill to Pasta Peak, then from Pasta Peak to Lizard Landing, and then back to Ho Hum Hill. How many miles did she drive in total?

	Ho Hum Hill	Anteater Alley	Lizard Landing	Vinegarville	Cheddarfield	Pasta Peak	Oopsburg	Raisin Ridge
Giggletown	124	129	136	152	167	175	179	203
Ho Hum Hill		113	121	140	155	169	182	194
Anteater Alley			137	154	178	183	195	217
Lizard Landing				152	174	181	200	226

2. How much further is a round-trip from Anteater Alley to Oopsburg than a round-trip from Giggletown to Cheddarfield?

3. Compare. Write $<$, $>$, or $=$ in the box.

a. $7 + 600 + 70 \ \boxed{\phantom{<}} \ 60 + 7 + 700$

b. $1000 + 100 \ \boxed{\phantom{<}} \ 800 + 300$

c. $2000 + 50 \ \boxed{\phantom{<}} \ 5000 + 200$

4. Write the time the clock shows.

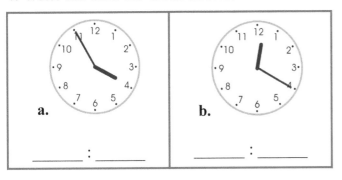

a. _____ : _____

b. _____ : _____

5. Estimate the total cost.

a bicycle, $256, and helmet, $64

   bicycle about $_____

   helmet about $_____

total cost about $ _____

6. Skip-count backwards.

587		575		

Skills Review 54

1. Write an addition or a subtraction for each problem. Use ? for the unknown thing.

a. Matthew bought a used car for $5,215 and now he has $2,830. How much money did Matthew have originally? _____ Solution: _____	**b.** Eggland Company has 1,250 hens. One day, 830 of the hens each laid an egg. How many hens didn't lay an egg? _____ Solution: _____

2. Calculate.

a. $25 - 3 \times 3 + 4 \times 2$	**b.** $9 + 7 \times (8 + 4)$

3. Draw oranges and half-oranges to complete the pictograph. Each picture of an orange means <u>four</u> pounds, and a picture of one-half of orange means half of that.

Pounds of Oranges Picked	
Eric	26
Mark	32
Jade	18
Leticia	34

Pounds of Oranges Picked	
Eric	
Mark	
Jade	
Leticia	

4. How much time passes during these intervals?

a. From 7:25 to 12:25
b. From 3:20 AM to 5:20 PM

5. How many half-dollars and/or quarters do you need to make these amounts?

a. 300 cents _____ half-dollars	**b.** 450 cents _____ half-dollars
c. 275 cents _____ half-dollars **and** _____ quarter(s)	

Skills Review 55

1. The picture shows how much money you have. Write how much you will have left if you buy the items listed.

If I buy:	I will have left:
a. shampoo for $3.95	$
b. gloves for $9.50	$

2. Solve for the part that is marked with "?".

total **1,285**		
625	248	?

3. Continue the patterns. They are actually certain multiplication tables!

a.		b.	
1		5	45
2			
3	36		
4		8	
5		9	81
6	72		
7			
8			

4. It is June 12th. Adrian and Carol's anniversary is July 28th. How many days is it until their anniversary?

5. Write the time using "a quarter past", "a quarter till", "half past", or "o'clock."

a. 1:15	**b.** 4:30	**c.** 9:45	**d.** 12:00

Skills Review 56

1. Add. It helps to first add the numbers which make ten (if any)!

a.
```
      2 4
  7 3 5 9
+   8 6 0
---------
```

b.
```
  3 0 7 4
      1 7 3
+ 5 2 8 6
---------
```

c.
```
  4 6 3 7
    1 5 0 8
+ 2 7 9 5
---------
```

2. Find the change. Also, find what coins and bills that could be used to make the change.

a. A blanket costs $18.65. You give $20.	**b.** Socks cost $4.48. You give $10.

3. Solve. Write a number sentence for each problem. Do not just write the answer.

a. Beatrice cut some cakes into eight pieces each and one cake into nine pieces. She ended up with a total of 49 pieces. How many cakes did she have?
b. Barry has 12 rows in his garden. He planted 11 plants each in five of the rows, 8 plants each in three of the rows, and 10 plants each in the rest of the rows. How many plants does Barry have in his garden?
c. Oh no! Nine hungry grasshoppers had a birthday party in Barry's garden and each one ate three of his plants. How many plants does Barry have left now?

Skills Review 57

1. Find the missing factors.

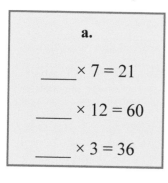

a.

_____ × 7 = 21

_____ × 12 = 60

_____ × 3 = 36

b.

9 × _____ = 18

2 × _____ = 22

5 × _____ = 40

c.

1 × _____ = 10

_____ × 6 = 42

10 × _____ = 50

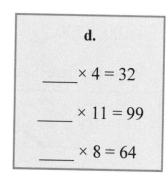

d.

_____ × 4 = 32

_____ × 11 = 99

_____ × 8 = 64

2. Subtract. Check by adding.

a.   6 0 3 0
        – 4 8 1 9   + _____

b.   9 4 0 1
        – 5 7 2 3   + _____

3. Megan started eating lunch at 12:08 and finished at 12:32. Gary started eating lunch at 12:23 and finished at 12:49. Who took a longer time to eat lunch?

How much longer?

4. Find the change.

a. <u>Price</u>: $6.85. Customer gave $10.

Change: $_____

b. <u>Price</u>: $13.60. Customer gave $20.

Change: $_____

Puzzle Corner   Which operations will make the number sentences true?

9 ☐ 7 ☐ 5 = 58   16 ☐ 2 ☐ 6 = 4   7 ☐ 8 ☐ 4 ☐ 9 = 20

Skills Review 58

1. Skip-count by one hundred.

4600, 4700, _____ , _____ , _____ , _____

2. Write the time the clock shows using the words "quarter past," "quarter till," "past," or "till."

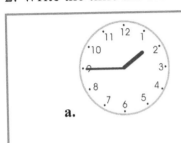

a. _____

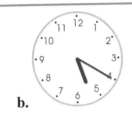

b. _____

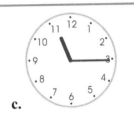

c. _____

3. Allison cut six cakes into eight pieces each and one cake into nine pieces. She served one piece each to 34 people. How many pieces of cake does she have left?

4. Damon bought a shirt for $15.95 and a hat for $7.99. He also bought a shirt that didn't have a price tag. He paid $36.44 in total for the three items. How much was the shirt that didn't have a price tag?

5. Solve.

a. $4,700 + \triangle = 5,300$

$\triangle =$ _____

b. $\triangle - 800 = 6,400$

$\triangle =$ _____

c. $12,000 - \triangle = 7,200$

$\triangle =$ _____

6. Write < or > between the numbers.

a. 3,281 ___ 3,481

b. 1,063 ___ 1,036

c. 7,510 ___ 7,095

d. 610 ___ 6,010

7. Round these numbers to the nearest hundred.

a. $8,439 \approx$ _____

b. $2,648 \approx$ _____

c. $6,763 \approx$ _____

Skills Review 59

1. First, estimate by rounding to the nearest hundred. Then find the exact total.

A used golf cart costs $3,738 and golf clubs cost $384.

My estimate: about $_____

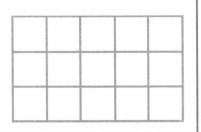

2. The bar graph shows how many pounds of fish were caught by the crews of four different fishing boats.

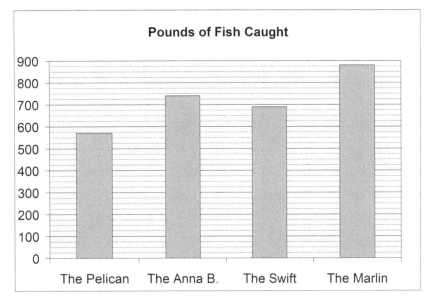

Pounds of Fish Caught

a. *About* how many pounds of fish did the crew of The Pelican and the crew of The Swift catch in total?

_____

b. *About* how many fewer pounds of fish did the crew of The Anna B. catch than the crew of The Marlin?

_____

3. Solve.

a. $4,700 + \triangle = 5,300$

$\triangle = $ _____

b. $\triangle - 800 = 6,400$

$\triangle = $ _____

4. Draw straight lines through the shape and divide it into an octagon and four triangles!

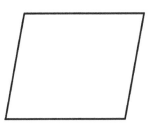

5. Add parentheses to each equation to make it true.

a. $25 - 9 \times 2 = 7$	b. $6 + 5 \times 4 - 4 = 0$	c. $6 \times 3 + 2 \times 2 - 4 = 18$

Skills Review 60

1. Multiply.

| **a.** $0 \times 0 =$ _____ | **b.** $593 \times 1 =$ _____ | **c.** $8 \times 4 =$ _____ | **d.** $6 \times 11 =$ _____ |

2. Rebecca made several bouquets for a wedding. She made seven bouquets of 12 flowers and nine bouquets of 10 flowers, and had seven flowers left over. How many flowers did she have originally?

3. Write the time the clock shows.

a. _____ : _____   **b.** _____ : _____   **c.** _____ : _____   **d.** _____ : _____

4. Draw three rhombi of different sizes.

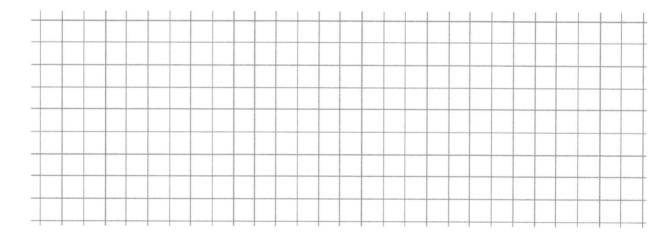

5. Fill in the number chart and count backwards by tens.

1 2 2 0	1 2 1 0			

Skills Review 61

1. Find the missing factors.

a.	b.	c.	d.
____ × 7 = 28	1 × ____ = 6	4 × ____ = 16	____ × 4 = 32
____ × 11 = 99	5 × ____ = 45	____ × 2 = 24	____ × 8 = 64
____ × 3 = 15	12 × ____ = 144	9 × ____ = 54	____ × 6 = 60

2. Find the perimeter...

  a. ...of a square with 9-inch sides

  b. ...of a rectangle with 8 cm and 14 cm sides

3. Solve the word problems.

a. Fiona had $198.32. Then she bought two puzzles for $14.50 each and a volleyball for $12.95. How much money does she have now?	**b.** Fiona paid with a $50 bill. What was her change?

Puzzle Corner   What numbers are missing?

7 ☐ 1 ☐	2 4 ☐ ☐	8 ☐ ☐ 6	☐ ☐ 4 7
− ☐ 5 ☐ 8	+ ☐ ☐ 7 9	− ☐ 2 7 ☐	+ 3 6 ☐ ☐
3 2 5 4	7 3 0 4	1 9 6 0	5 4 4 5

Skills Review 62

1. How much money? Write the amount in cents.

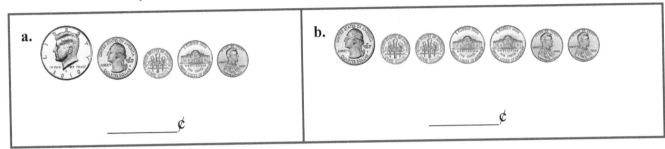

a. _____¢

b. _____¢

2. Add or subtract using Roman numerals. Write your answer as a Roman numeral.

a. CCCXIV + LXXX

b. CLXVII + XC

c. CCLXXIV − LX

d. CXLVI − XXXVII

3. Here, *three* parts make up a whole. Solve for the part that is marked with "?".

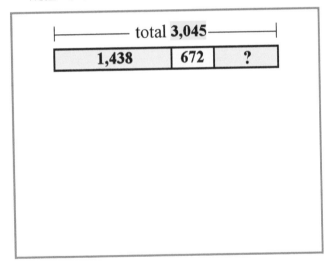

4. Write the time the clock shows. Then write the time 20 minutes *earlier* in the box beneath.

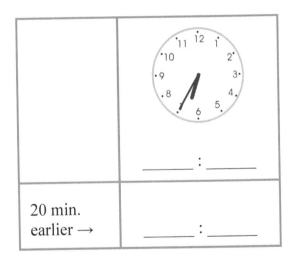

5. Solve. Write an addition with an unknown for each problem.

The perimeter of this rectangle is 40 cm. Its one side is 8 cm. How long is the other side?

_____

Solution: _?_ = _____

?

8 cm

Skills Review 63

1. The pictograph shows how many hamburgers were sold at a restaurant over a four-day period.

   a. How many more hamburgers did the restaurant sell on Saturday than on Thursday?

   _____

   b. How many hamburgers did the restaurant sell in total over the four-day period?

   _____

Hamburgers Sold at a Restaurant	
Wednesday	🍔🍔🍔🍔🍔🍔🍔🍔
Thursday	🍔🍔🍔🍔🍔🍔🍔
Friday	🍔🍔🍔🍔🍔🍔🍔🍔🍔🍔
Saturday	🍔🍔🍔🍔🍔🍔🍔🍔🍔🍔🍔🍔🍔🍔

🍔 = 10 hamburgers   🍔 = 5 hamburgers

2. Write a multiplication to find the area. "A" means area.

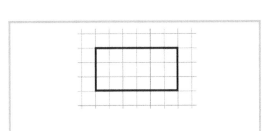

_____ × _____ = _____

A = _____ square units.

3. Write the time using "a quarter past," "a quarter till," "half past," or "o'clock."

a.

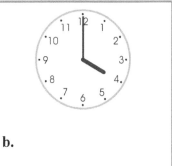

b.

4. Write an addition or a subtraction for each problem. Use ? for the unknown thing.

a. Halfway through a game, Ann had 850 points. A couple of turns later, she had half that many more. Oh no! On the next turn, she landed on a penalty space and lost a lot of points! After that, she had 825 points. How many points did she lose?

b. Bryan bought a laptop for $1,250 and a camera for $765, and now he has $3,098 left. How much money did he have originally?

Skills Review 64

1. The mileage chart shows the distance between some cities in Asia.

	Beijing	Bangkok	Tokyo	Seoul	New Delhi
Hong Kong	1,958	1,727	2,878	2,087	3,750
Beijing		3,294	2,091	952	3,778
Bangkok			4,600	3,720	2,596
Tokyo				1,152	5,834

a. Helen flew round-trip from Hong Kong to Tokyo. How many miles did she travel?

b. How many miles farther is a round-trip flight from Tokyo to New Delhi than a round-trip flight from Beijing to New Delhi?

2. Multiply.

a.

$3 \times 6 =$ _____

$7 \times 12 =$ _____

$6 \times 7 =$ _____

b.

$12 \times 11 =$ _____

$9 \times 9 =$ _____

$9 \times 3 =$ _____

c.

$8 \times 10 =$ _____

$7 \times 2 =$ _____

$5 \times 8 =$ _____

d.

$7 \times 9 =$ _____

$12 \times 5 =$ _____

$6 \times 4 =$ _____

3. Solve.

a. $8 \times 4 - (4 + 5)$	**b.** $43 + 3 - 9 \times 3$

4. Write a number sentence for the total area, thinking of one rectangle or two.

_____ × (_____ + _____) = _____ × _____ + _____ × _____

area of the whole rectangle   area of the first part   area of the second part

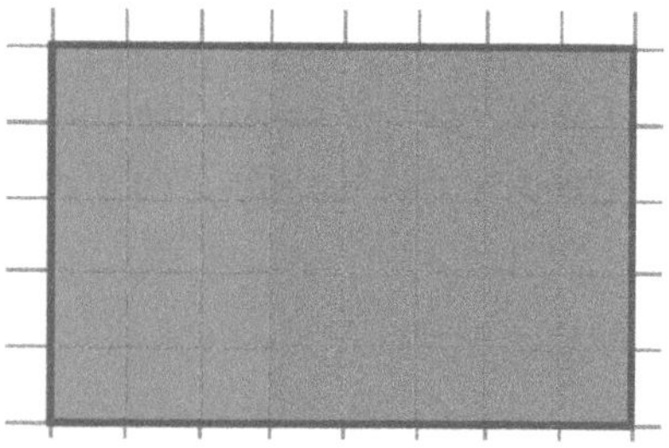

Skills Review 65

1. The picture shows how much money you have. Write how much you will have left if you buy the items listed.

If I buy:	I will have left:
a. a clock for $9.95	$
b. a hat for $6.70	$

2. Solve 5 × 50 by dividing this rectangle into parts. There are several ways to do it!

Parts: _____. The total area is_____.

If possible, compare the way you did it with the way your friend or teacher did it.

3. Solve. Write a number sentence. Do not just write the answer.

Megan served seven trays of mini pizzas to people at a party. Each tray had nine pizzas on it. At the end of the party, there were six pizzas left. How many pizzas were eaten?

 Mrs. Baker asked 12 of her students to each bring six feathers to class the next day for a craft project. Some students forgot to bring any, and one only brought half as many as he was supposed to, so there were only 57 feathers. How many students forgot?

Skills Review 66

1. Find the area of the flower garden.

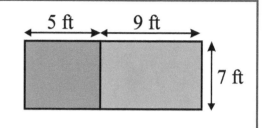

2. Number the men with ordinal numbers starting *from the right*. Use the picture to help answer the questions.

   a. Mr. Adams is 14th in the line. Mr. Elliot is in front of him and there are nine people between them. What is Mr. Elliot's position in line?

   b. Mr. Jackson is 7th in line. Mr. Craig is behind him and there are five people between them. What is Mr. Craig's position in line?

3. Using a calendar, find the given dates.

   a. September 26th

      3 weeks earlier: _____

   b. February 17th

      8 weeks later: _____

   c. December 23rd

      4 weeks earlier: _____

4. Round the numbers to the nearest hundred.

   a.

   $932 \approx$ _____

   b.

   $8,351 \approx$ _____

   c.

   $3,049 \approx$ _____

5. Fill in the missing cent-amount.

| **a.** 73¢ + _____¢ = $1 | **b.** $6.14 + _____¢ = $7 | **c.** $2.38 + _____¢ = $5 |

Skills Review 67

1. Estimate the answer by rounding the numbers to the nearest hundred.
   Then find the exact answer.

   > A used motorcycle costs $3,732 and a jacket costs $238.
   > First, estimate the total bill. Then find the exact total.
   >
   > My estimate: about $_____
   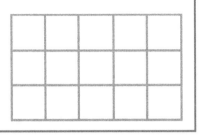

2. The graph shows how many passengers
   are riding on five different trains.

   a. Which two trains are carrying
   a total of *about* 370 passengers
   <u>between the two of them</u>?

   _____

   b. How many more passengers is
   Train 4 carrying than Train 1?

   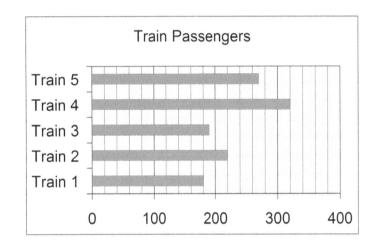

3. Write < or > between the numbers.

   a. 2,156   2,165   **b.** 3,900   3,090   **c.** 7,250   7,205

4. Make two different rectangles that
   each have an area of 28 square units.

   Draw them in the grid. Write their
   side lengths in the table.

	first side	**second side**	**area**
Rectangle 1			28 square units
Rectangle 2			28 square units

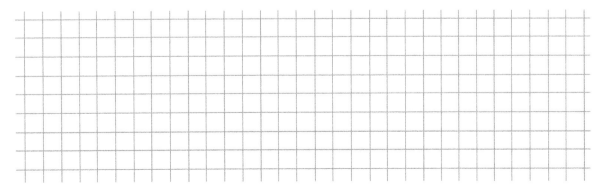

Skills Review 68

1. Write the time in words. Use the expressions "quarter past," "quarter till," "till," or "past."

    a. 8:20 _____

    b. 11:45 _____

    c. 10:15 _____

    d. 1:50 _____

2. Find the perimeter. Notice: some side lengths are not given! Don't forget to use the unit of measurement in your answer.

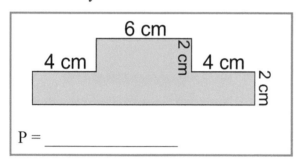

    P = _____

3. Solve.

    a. $3{,}700 + \triangle = 4{,}300$

    $\triangle =$ _____

    b. $6{,}200 - \triangle = 3{,}900$

    $\triangle =$ _____

4. Complete:

    a. If a shape has THREE vertices (corners) and three sides, it is a _____.

    b. If a shape has FOUR vertices and four sides, it is a _____.

    c. If a shape has FIVE vertices and five sides, it is a _____.

    d. If a shape has SIX vertices and six sides, it is a _____.

5. Solve.

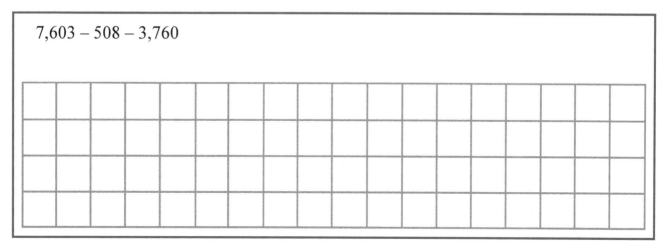

$$7{,}603 - 508 - 3{,}760$$

Skills Review 69

1. Write how many half-dollars or how many quarters you need to make these amounts.

a. 850 cents	**b.** 675 cents	**c.** 500 cents	**d.** 425 cents
_____ half-dollars	_____ quarters	_____ half-dollars	_____ quarters

2. Color the shapes that are rhombi.

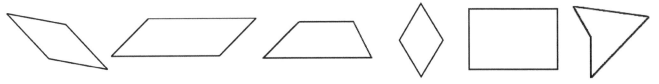

3. Add.

a. $4000 + 70 + 600 + 3 =$ _____	**b.** $9000 + 5 + 700 =$ _____

4. Draw lines using a ruler.

   a. 2 3/4 inches long

   b. 3 1/2 inches long

5. Solve the word problems.

a. Karen made six lists with 12 words in each list. Then she erased two words from three of the lists. How many words does she have left?

b. Bruce and five of his friends want to buy a microscope that costs $124. Bruce has $18, and each of his friends have $11. How much more money do they need?

Skills Review 70

1. Write any multiplication problem you like where the answer is between 10 and 32. Write it in two ways. Then draw jumps on the number line to illustrate.

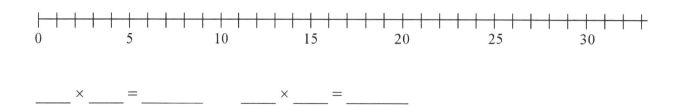

_____ × _____ = _____   _____ × _____ = _____

2. Compare the chart with the pictograph. Is the chart correct? If not, cross out the incorrect numbers and write the correct ones. One shell picture means 6 shells. Half of a shell picture means 3 shells.

Seashells collected	
Kayla	30
Dylan	20
Brenna	38

Seashells collected	
Kayla	🐚 🐚 🐚 🐚 🐚
Dylan	🐚 🐚 🐚 🐚
Brenna	🐚 🐚 🐚 🐚 🐚 🐚 🐚

3. Match.

rectangular pyramid

square pyramid

tetrahedron

4. Write using Roman numerals.

a. 244
b. 527
c. 392
d. 184

5. Measure the following items, using a centimeter-millimeter ruler. If the item is not exactly as long as the markers on the ruler, choose the nearest mark.

Item	Length
nail clippers	
fork	

Skills Review 71

1. Solve for the part that is marked with "?".

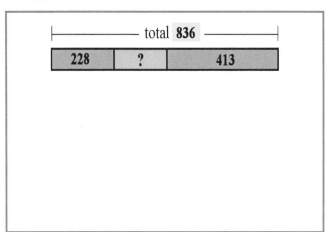

2. Multiply.

a.

$7 \times 4 =$ _____

$9 \times 9 =$ _____

$2 \times 3 =$ _____

$6 \times 5 =$ _____

$11 \times 8 =$ _____

b.

$12 \times 2 =$ _____

$1 \times 0 =$ _____

$9 \times 6 =$ _____

$5 \times 12 =$ _____

$7 \times 7 =$ _____

3. Celia measured the length of some scraps of cloth. She recorded her results in a **line plot** below. For each scrap of cloth, she put an "x" mark above the number line to show how many inches long it was.

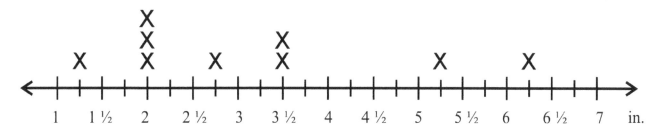

a. How long is the scrap of cloth whose X-mark is between 2 1/2 and 3 inches?

b. How many of the scraps are at least 3 1/2 inches long?

4. Write the cent amounts as dollar amounts, and vice versa.

a. 27¢ = $_____	**b.** $5.82 = _____ ¢	**c.** 3¢ = $_____

5. The Hill family has a rectangular swimming pool with a perimeter of 108 feet. One side measures 36 feet. How long is the other side?

Skills Review 72

1. Draw a rectangle that corresponds with the problem. Fill in the blanks.

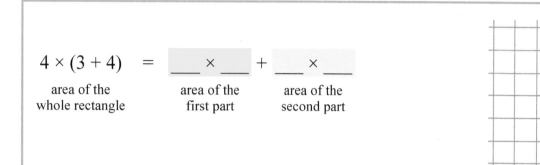

$$4 \times (3 + 4) \quad = \quad \underline{} \times \underline{} \quad + \quad \underline{} \times \underline{}$$

area of the whole rectangle   area of the first part   area of the second part

2. A ship had 1,330 passengers. It stopped at Port Pleasant and 80 people got off. Then it stopped at Port Purple and 50 people got on. How many passengers does the ship have now?

3. Marianne's birthday is August 19th and Justin's is three weeks later. When is Justin's birthday?

4. Round these numbers to the nearest hundred.

| **a.** 4,638 ≈ _____ | **b.** 7,351 ≈ _____ | **c.** 2,572 ≈ _____ |

5. Fill in the blanks, using the units in., ft, or mi.

a. Jenny is 7____ taller than Kay.   **b.** Aaron drove 50 ____ an hour.

c. The pool is 12 ____ deep.   **d.** Andrea is 4 ____ tall.

Puzzle Corner   What numbers are missing?

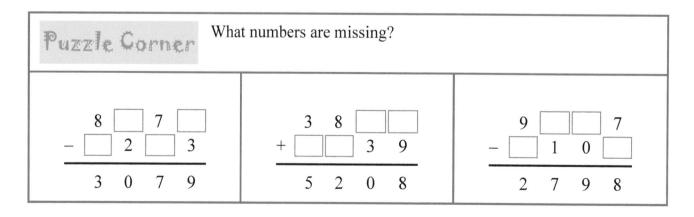

Skills Review 73

1. Multiply.

| **a.** $10 \times 30 =$ _____ | **b.** $100 \times 7 =$ _____ | **c.** $5 \times 60 =$ _____ |

2. **a.** Brenda was supposed to arrive at Ashley's house at 2:30, but she got there 15 minutes early. What time did Brenda arrive?

   b. Brenda stayed at Ashley's house for 2 1/2 hours. What time did she leave?

3. Find the change. Also, find what coins and bills that could be used to make the change.

a. A camera costs $35.80. You give $50.	**b.** Shoes cost $16.48. You give $20.

4. Calculate.

a. $7 \times (15 - 9) + 8$	**b.** $(23 - 14) \times (6 + 3)$

5. Work out these "line additions". You can use a ruler to help, or you can draw the lines.

| **a.** 2 3/4 in. + 7 1/4 in. = _____ | **b.** 3/4 in. + 3/4 in. = _____ |

Exercise 6 is optional.

6. Convert between meters and centimeters. Remember that 1 meter is 100 cm.

| **a.** 3 m 74 cm = _____ cm | **b.** 8 m 9 cm = _____ cm | **c.** 6 m 94 cm = _____ cm |

Skills Review 74

1. Underline or circle whether the number is even or odd. If the number is even, write it as "two times the number that was doubled." If the number is odd, do nothing.

a. 64 is even/odd	b. 98 is even/odd	c. 45 is even/odd
2 × _____	2 × _____	2 × _____

2. Draw lines using a ruler.

   a. 125 mm

   b. 7 cm 8 mm

3. Which is the best estimate of weight?

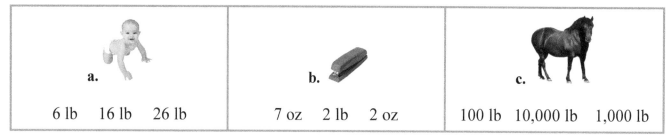

a.	b.	c.
6 lb 16 lb 26 lb	7 oz 2 lb 2 oz	100 lb 10,000 lb 1,000 lb

4. Solve. Write a number sentence for each problem. Do not just write the answer.

a. Carl bought seven packages of 5 razors and four packages of 12 razors. Then, he gave eight razors to his brother. How many razors does he have left?

b. Amy's neighbor offered to pay her $9 an hour for helping plant some trees. Amy worked for six hours. Her neighbor gave her some extra money, so she earned $65. How much extra did she get?

c. Clara picked some tomatoes and put them into eight bags, with six tomatoes in each bag. Then, Clara's little sister came along and put three more tomatoes into each bag. How many tomatoes were there in total?

Skills Review 75

1. The clock shows the time now. Write the later times.

NOW:

- 5 minutes later _____ : _____   • 20 minutes later _____ : _____

- 10 minutes later _____ : _____   • 25 minutes later _____ : _____

2. Fill in the blanks with a reasonable unit of weight (either g or kg).

   a. Carmen needs 2 _____ of lemons to make lemonade for a party.

   b. The treasure chest weighed 150 _____.

   c. Melissa ate 35 _____ of chocolate.

3. Find the missing factors.

a.	**b.**	**c.**	**d.**
_____ × 9 = 81	12 × _____ = 60	3 × _____ = 27	_____ × 4 = 24

4. Grace bought sunglasses for $12.35 and lip balm for $3.28. Find the total cost and her change from $20.

5. How many jars of jam that cost $2.98 each can you buy with $30?

6. Find the areas of the rectangles. Be very careful about the unit you need to use, whether square centimeters (cm^2), square meters (m^2), square inches (in^2), or square feet (ft^2).

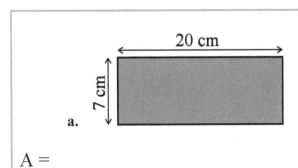

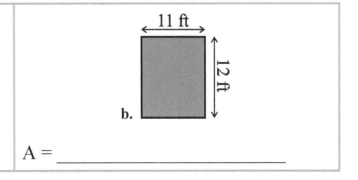

a.   20 cm   7 cm   A = _____

b.   11 ft   12 ft   A = _____

Skills Review 76

1. Fill in with the words cup, pint, or quart.

   a. Mom made 4 _____s of tea to serve to 12 people.

   b. The cake recipe called for 3 _____s of flour.

   c. Mary wanted more than a cup of pudding, so she ate a _____ .

2. Add and subtract. Estimate first by rounding the numbers to the nearest hundred.

<table>
<tr>
<td>

a. Estimate:

   4,875   +   2,919

     ↓   ↓

        +   = _____

</td>
<td>

Calculate exactly:

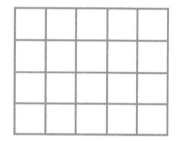

</td>
</tr>
<tr>
<td>

b. Estimate:

   6,501   –   938

     ↓   ↓

        –   = _____

</td>
<td>

Calculate exactly:

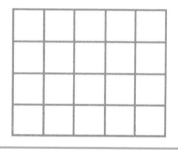

</td>
</tr>
</table>

3. Write as dollar amounts.

seven quarters	two dimes, four pennies and a nickel	five quarters and three nickels
a. $_____	**b.** $_____	**c.** $_____

Exercise 4 is optional.

4. Convert between feet and inches.   12 inches makes 1 foot.

a. 4 ft 9 in. = _____ in.	**b.** 12 ft 6 in. = _____ in.	**c.** 8 ft = _____ in.

Skills Review 77

1. Solve (find the number that the symbol stands for).

a. $3{,}200 - \triangle = 2{,}700$	**b.** $4{,}900 + \triangle = 8{,}100$	**c.** $\triangle - 2{,}300 = 6{,}800$
$\triangle =$ _____	$\triangle =$ _____	$\triangle =$ _____

2. Add the dollar amounts. In **c.**, write the amounts of money in the grid before adding.

a.

```
  $ 9 . 8 4
    7 . 3 0
 + 4 0 . 1 6
```

b.

```
  $ 5 . 9 5
    5 . 4 4
    8 . 2 0
 +  2 . 6 2
```

c. $\$57.03 + \$6.58 + \$5.72$

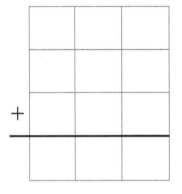

3. Solve the word problems. Write a division or a multiplication for each problem.

The box ☐ is for the × or ÷ symbol.

a. Carl is making teams of six. How many people are there in six teams? 	**b.** Carl is making teams of six. How many teams can he make with 24 people? 

Exercises 4 and 5 are optional.

4. Heather made 3 liters of orange juice and poured it into 300 ml bottles. How many bottles did she fill?

5. Remember that 1 liter is 1,000 milliliters. Convert between liters and milliliters.

a.	**b.**	**c.**
5 L = _____ ml	2 L 600 ml = _____ ml	7 L 40 ml = _____ ml

Skills Review 78

1. Of the 5,853 people who participated
   in a marathon, only 5,708 of them were
   able to run the entire distance.
   How many people had to drop out?

2. Write the time the clock shows.

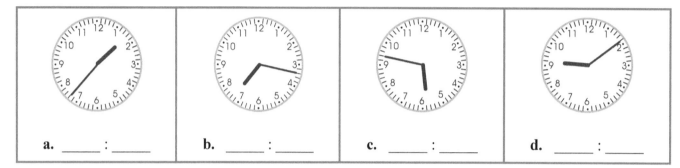

a. _____ : _____   b. _____ : _____   c. _____ : _____   d. _____ : _____

3. Write these numbers in order from the least to the greatest.

   3048   4138   5280   3012   5028   3480   4152

   _____ < _____ < _____ < _____ < _____ < _____ < _____

4. For each division, think of the corresponding multiplication and solve.

a. $48 \div 12 =$ _____	b. $56 \div 7 =$ _____	c. $28 \div 4 =$ _____
____ $\times 12 = 48$	____ $\times 7 =$ ____	____ $\times$ ____ $=$ ____

5. Measure the following items using a ruler that has the ¼ , ½, and ¾ inch marks (quarters
   of an inch). If the item is not exactly as long as the markers on the ruler show, choose the
   nearest mark as the length, and write "about 5 ¼ inches," *etc.* The third item can be
   anything you choose.

Item	Length
your shoe	
a book	

Skills Review 79

1. Write how many half-dollars and how many quarters you need to make these amounts.

a. 475 cents _____ half-dollars **and** _____ quarter(s)	**b.** 725 cents _____ half-dollars **and** _____ quarter(s)

2. The bar graph shows five people who are each saving their money.

   a. _About_ how much more money has Shane saved than Calista?

   _____

   b. Does Leslie have enough money to buy a car that costs $4,500?

   If not, _about_ how much more money does she need?

   _____

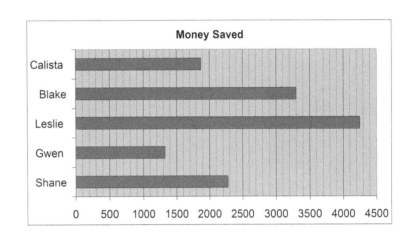

3. **a.** Measure the sides of this rectangle in centimeters and millimeters.

   b. What is its perimeter?

4. Write a multiplication _and_ a division for each situation.

a. Bert bought six hammers for $9 each.	_____ × _____ = _____ _____ ÷ _____ = _____
b. Joy and 11 of her friends shared 48 cookies equally.	_____ × _____ = _____ _____ ÷ _____ = _____

Skills Review 80

1. Find the unknown numbers (marked by a circle or ?).

a. $\bigcirc \div 8 = 12$ $\bigcirc =$ _____	b. $42 \div \bigcirc = 6$ $\bigcirc =$ _____	c. $54 \div 9 = \bigcirc$ $\bigcirc =$ _____	d. $\bigcirc \div 5 = 7$ $\bigcirc =$ _____

2. Write the time as *hours* : *minutes*.

a. half past 11	b. 25 till 3	c. a quarter till 1	d. 20 past 5
_____ : _____	_____ : _____	_____ : _____	_____ : _____

3. Measure several small objects of different lengths to the nearest quarter inch, such as a spoon, tweezers, *etc.* Write the lengths below.

_____ in., _____ in., _____ in., _____ in., _____ in.

_____ in., _____ in., _____ in., _____ in., _____ in.

Now, make a line plot about the objects you measured. Write an "X" mark for each object.

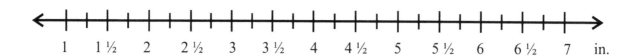

1   1 ½   2   2 ½   3   3 ½   4   4 ½   5   5 ½   6   6 ½   7   in.

4. Write using Roman numerals.

a. 215	b. 544	c. 371
216	545	372
217	546	373

Skills Review 81

1. Oopsburg had 2,348 inhabitants. Then, over a six-month period, seven people moved away and three people died. After that, how many inhabitants did Oopsburg have?

2. How much time passes during these intervals?

a. From 2:30 AM to 1:00 PM
b. From 7:35 PM to 8:35 AM

3. For each division, think of the corresponding multiplication and solve.

a. $108 \div 12 =$ _____   _____ × _____ = _____
b. $49 \div 7 =$ _____   _____ × _____ = _____

4. Fill in the blanks, using the units "cm", "km", "mm", or "m".

  a. The pickup truck is 5 _____ long.   **b.** The West family drove 35 _____ to the zoo.

  c. My book is 24 _____ wide.   **d.** Robert's house is 15 _____ wide.

5. Solve. Write a division or a multiplication for each problem.

a. Jason planted 28 plants in rows of seven. How many rows did he plant? 	**b.** Josh planted his plants in nine rows of six. How many plants did he have? 
c. Evelyn baked six pies and cut each one into 12 pieces. How many pieces of pie did she have? 	**d.** Lola baked some pies and cut each one into nine pieces, making a total of 63 pieces. How many pies did she bake?

Skills Review 82

1. Divide. CROSS OUT all the problems that are impossible. Think about sharing apples.

a. $7 \div 0 =$ _____	**b.** $12 \div 12 =$ _____	**c.** $9 \div 1 =$ _____	**d.** $0 \div 8 =$ _____

2. Write the weight the scales show, in pounds. Note: The numbers for the pounds are red.

a.

_____ lbs

b.

_____ lbs

3. Calculate.

a. $82 - (6 \times 9) + 7$	**b.** $50 - 3 + 11 \times 4$

4. Complete the next whole thousand.

a. $2200 +$ _____ $=$ _____	**b.** $9600 +$ _____ $=$ _____

5. Jocelyn had 64 roses that she used
   to make bouquets of 8 flowers each.
   How many bouquets did she make?

6. Find the area.

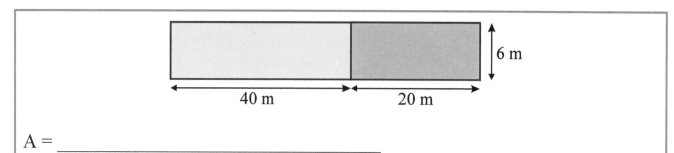

A = _____

Skills Review 83

1. Solve. Remember the order of operations.

a. $618 - (189 + 235) =$ _____

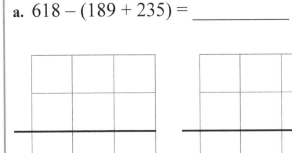

b. $803 - 394 + 217 =$ _____

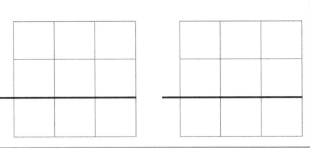

2. Marissa and Brad visited their grandma for three
   weeks and then returned home on August 18th.
   What was the date they arrived at Grandma's house?

3. Round these numbers to the nearest hundred.

a. $7,352 \approx$ _____

b. $9,438 \approx$ _____

c. $2,861 \approx$ _____

4. Divide and indicate the remainders.

a. $19 \div 6 =$ ____ R____

   $20 \div 6 =$ ____ R____

b. $15 \div 8 =$ ____ R____

   $30 \div 8 =$ ____ R____

c. $56 \div 6 =$ ____ R____

   $59 \div 6 =$ ____ R____

Exercise 5 and Puzzle Corner are optional. Remember, there are 1,000 milliliters in one liter.

5. Bianca squeezed three liters of orange juice
   and poured it into 250-ml glasses. How many
   glasses did she fill?

How many pints of water fill a 3-gallon bucket?

Puzzle Corner

Hint: Think first how many pints of water fit into 1 gallon, 2 gallons, and so on.

Skills Review 84

1. The perimeter of this square is 28 cm.
   How long is the side of the square?

?

2. Multiply.

| **a.** $8 \times 40 =$ _____ | **b.** $90 \times 5 =$ _____ | **c.** $4 \times 70 =$ _____ |

3. Find the total area.

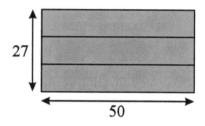

27

50

4. Vanessa bought a teddy bear for $8.35 and
   a night light for $3.28. She paid with $20.
   How much change did she get back?

5. Brandon bought a kite for $11.70, and paid with a $10 bill
   and a $5 bill. He got back two $1 bills, three quarters, four
   dimes, and a nickel. Did he receive the correct change?
   If not, how much change should he have gotten?

6. Divide and find the remainder by subtracting.

a. $7 \overline{)3\ 1}$ **b.** $9 \overline{)6\ 0}$ **c.** $6 \overline{)5\ 0}$ **d.** $8 \overline{)7\ 4}$

I am in the table of seven. If you add my digits,
you get one half of 24.

Skills Review 85

1. Color the parts to illustrate the fraction.

a.   b.   c.   d.   e.   f.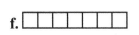

$\dfrac{5}{8}$ $\dfrac{8}{10}$ $\dfrac{2}{6}$ $\dfrac{1}{5}$ $\dfrac{3}{4}$ $\dfrac{6}{7}$

2. Write the weight that each scales shows, in grams.

a.

b.

_____ grams   _____ grams

3. Find the missing numbers in these divisions. Check by writing a matching multiplication.

a. _____ ÷ 11 = 8	b. _____ ÷ 6 = 6	c. 72 ÷ _____ = 9
_____ × _____ = _____	_____ × _____ = _____	_____ × _____ = _____

4. The Benson family's rectangular swimming
   pool is 15 feet wide and 30 feet long.
   What is its perimeter?

5. Solve. Optionally, write a number sentence.

Brenda baked 28 ginger cookies and 42
oatmeal cookies and packaged them in
packages of seven. How many packages of
cookies were there, in total?

Skills Review 86

1. Find the total cost of buying the things listed. Add mentally if you can.

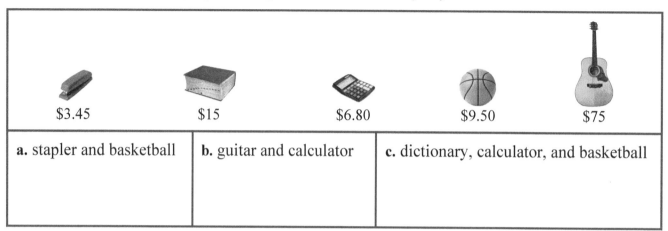

$3.45	$15	$6.80

a. stapler and basketball	**b.** guitar and calculator	**c.** dictionary, calculator, and basketball

2. Divide the number line from 0 to 1 into equal parts. Then mark the fraction on it.

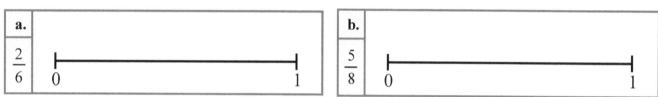

3. Write a number sentence for the total area, thinking of one rectangle or two.

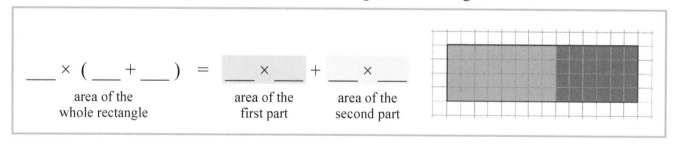

___ × (___ + ___) = ___ × ___ + ___ × ___

area of the whole rectangle   area of the first part   area of the second part

4. Write or say a *division* story problem about 32 goldfish and some children.

5. Divide.

a. 48 ÷ 8 = _____	**b.** 27 ÷ 3 = _____	**c.** 50 ÷ 5 = _____

Skills Review 87

1. Subtract. Check by adding.

a.
```
   4 0 1 0
 − 1 8 2 5     +
```
_____   _____

b.
```
   7 0 0 2
 − 4 7 3 9     +
```
_____   _____

2. Starting at the top, find your way through the maze by coloring the number that is **double** the previous number.

18	12	15	13	20
27	36	25	29	23
69	72	75	66	71
142	137	144	135	148
279	288	263	287	251

3. Divide. CROSS OUT any problems that are impossible.

a. $30 \div 5 =$ _____

b. $0 \div 7 =$ _____

c. $10 \div 1 =$ _____

d. $40 \div 0 =$ _____

4. Find an empty one-gallon milk jug, a pint jar, and a cup.

   a. Fill the <u>pint</u> jar with water. Pour it all into the one-gallon jug. Repeat until the one-gallon jug is full.

   It takes _____ pints of water to fill a one-gallon jug.

   b. Find out how many cups it takes to fill the pint jar.

   c. Now think. How many cups does it take to fill the gallon jug?

5. Draw pie pictures to illustrate these mixed numbers.

a. $3\frac{2}{5}$	**b.** $5\frac{6}{8}$

Skills Review 88

1. Shade the parts for the first fraction. Shade the same *amount* in the second picture. Write the second fraction.

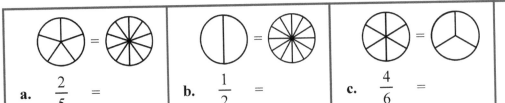

a. $\dfrac{2}{5}$ =	**b.** $\dfrac{1}{2}$ =
c. $\dfrac{4}{6}$ =	**d.** $\dfrac{6}{8}$ =

2. Compare. Write $<$, $>$, or $=$ in the box.

   a. $300 + 5000 \;\boxed{}\; 500 + 3000$

   b. $70 + 5 + 2000 \;\boxed{}\; 2000 + 7 + 50$

3. Solve. Write a number sentence for each problem. Do not just write the answer.

   a. Bob, Dave, Ken, and Joy each bought six plums. They put them all together and shared them equally with Joe, Beth, Hugh, and Faye. How many plums did each one get?

   b. Jay worked nine hours for $12 an hour. Then, he took his earnings and bought a skateboard for $39. How much money does he have left?

   c. Dustin gave eight stickers each to Holly and Ken, and five stickers each to Calvin, Lisa, Bonnie, and Eric. He had 29 stickers left. How many stickers did Dustin have originally?

Problem 4 is optional. Remember that 1 liter is 1,000 milliliters.

4. Karen made four liters of lemonade to sell at her lemonade stand. She sold nine 300 ml glasses of lemonade. How many milliliters of lemonade did she have left?

Skills Review 89

1. Divide.

a. $8\overline{)3\ 9}$ b. $3\overline{)7\ 1}$ c. $6\overline{)5\ 5}$ d. $11\overline{)6\ 9}$

2. Compare the fractions. Think carefully.

a. $\dfrac{7}{6}$ ☐ $\dfrac{3}{3}$ b. $\dfrac{2}{5}$ ☐ $\dfrac{4}{5}$ c. $\dfrac{4}{8}$ ☐ $\dfrac{6}{12}$ d. $\dfrac{1}{4}$ ☐ $\dfrac{1}{3}$

3. Solve. Write a division or a multiplication for each problem.

a. Greg earns $8 per hour. How much does he earn in nine hours? _____ ☐ _____ = _____	**b.** At $8 per hour, how many hours does Greg need to work to earn $88? _____ ☐ _____ = _____
c. Alicia can buy a bag of apples for $9. How many bags can she buy with $36? _____ ☐ _____ = _____	**d.** Alicia can buy a bag of apples for $9. She bought six bags. How much did she pay? _____ ☐ _____ = _____

4. Using a calendar, find out the later or earlier dates.

a. February 9th

7 weeks earlier: _____

b. October 22nd

5 weeks later: _____

5. Write these both as mixed numbers AND as fractions.

a.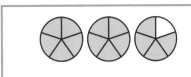

b.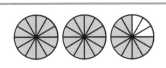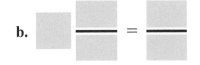

c.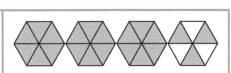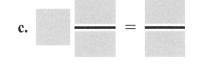

Skills Review 90

1. Write a multiplication _and_ a division for the situation.

Mom sewed six buttons each on seven shirts.	_____ × _____ = _____
	_____ ÷ _____ = _____

2. Estimate by rounding the numbers to the nearest hundred. Then, calculate the exact answer.

Estimation:	**Exact calculation:**
9,280 – 5,765	9 2 8 0
↓ ↓	– 5 7 6 5
_____ – _____ = _____	

3. Write the ending time or the starting time.

a. 2:55 → _____	**b.** _____ → 7:10	**c.** 9:40 → _____
55 minutes	40 minutes	35 minutes

4. Kayla baked two cakes of equal size. She cut one in six equal pieces and the other one in 12 equal pieces. Bruce ate 2/6 of the cake that was cut in six pieces.

   a. Draw the two cakes.
   Then color in what Bruce ate.

   b. How many pieces of the other cake would Kayla have to eat in order to eat the same amount of cake as Bruce?

Puzzle Corner   Which operations will make the number sentences true?

62 ☐ 9 ☐ 5 = 17   12 ☐ 4 ☐ 9 = 57   7 ☐ 8 ☐ 6 ☐ 6 = 51

CPSIA information can be obtained
at www.ICGtesting.com
Printed in the USA
FSHW022046050321
79180FS